LIFE SKILLS ATTITUDES
On the Job

Margaret M. Brewner

William C. McMahon

Kathleen A. Paris

Michael P. Roche

CONTENTS

INTRODUCTION

Life Skills Attitudes On the Job will show you how to be successful at work.

Getting and holding a job requires more than basic skills such as working a cash register, driving a van, or filing papers. Companies want employees who know how to follow directions. An employer always wants the people who work for him or her to be responsible. And everyone prefers workers who can get along with others.

Employers look for certain signs in your work to show them that you know these things. Unless you are an experienced worker, you may not know what your boss expects. As a beginning worker, you can make your job go smoothly if you know what *attitudes* will help. This book is about these attitudes.

You can get started right on the next page. It begins with the first thing an employer wants—an honest worker.

1. BEING HONEST
On the Job

WHAT'S BEING HONEST ALL ABOUT?

Sometimes things we do are dishonest. There are many ways that a person might be dishonest. Below is an honesty grid to show you some of these ways.

HONESTY GRID

	Time	Money	Products	People
Steal	Marty		Terry	
Lie				Lee
Cheat				Chris

Marty is someone who steals time. This means that he fools around or wastes time when he should be working. Since the boss is paying for time worked, we call a person like Marty a "time thief."

Terry is someone who takes things from work. A person like Terry might take office supplies, uniforms or equipment. These things cost the employer money.

Lee is someone who lies to people. Some of the things a person like Lee might lie about are:
   excuses for coming to work late
   making a mistake (blaming someone else)
   reasons for not showing up for work

Chris is someone who cheats other people. A person like Chris might cheat people out of their money or something else they own.

Read the stories on the next page. See if you can show where each person would be on the Honesty Grid. Look carefully. Sometimes you will have to fill in more than one space for a person.

HONESTY GRID

	Time	Money	Products	People
Steal				
Lie				
Cheat				

1. Joe works every day from 5 P.M. until 9 P.M. Last Friday his friends asked him to play cards at 7 P.M. Joe told his boss that he had to leave work early to babysit.

    Where is Joe on the Honesty Grid?

2. Victor is a busboy in a restaurant. While clearing the tables, he saw money that was left for the waitress. "Why should she get all of the tips? I do some of the work, too," he said to himself. So he put some of the tip money into his pocket when no one was looking.

    Where is Victor on the Honesty Grid?

3. Ana has been working at Brown's Clothing Store for one year. Today her friend, Sue, came in to buy a dress. The dress cost $10.00, but Sue only had $8.00. She asked Ana to ring the dress up for $8.00. Ana did not want to lose a friend, so she rang the dress up for $8.00.

    Where is Ana on the Honesty Grid?

4. Sandy is a cashier and is always very careful to give the right change. She thinks she is an honest worker. But Sandy often fools around and talks with her friends when they come into the store.

    Where is Sandy on the Honesty Grid?

5. ACE Factory is hiring workers. The want-ad says you must be 18 years old. Steve is only 17, but he would really like the job. He tells the boss that he is 18.

    Where is Steve on the Honesty Grid?

6. Kim is a cashier at a restaurant. Mr. and Mrs. Blum's dinner bill adds up to $20.00. Kim tells them that the bill is $21.00.

    Where is Kim on the Honesty Grid?

6

CLOUD QUESTIONS

Most of the time, being dishonest only gets you into trouble. What do you think the people you just read about are saying now? Fill in the empty clouds.

1. Joe told the boss he had to leave work early to babysit.

Hey, Joe, someone came in to give you some money. He said you won it playing cards Friday night. I though you told me you had to babysit.

BOSS

JOE

2. Victor took some of the waitress's tip money.

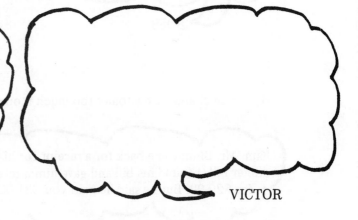

Victor, I saw you put some money into your pocket when you were clearing the table. The customer told me that he left a $1.00 tip. Now there is only 50¢ here.

WAITRESS

VICTOR

3. Ana didn't make her friend pay the full price for a dress.

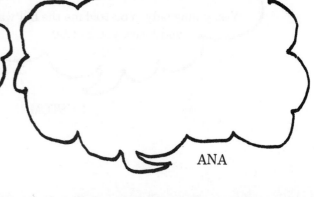

Ana, how come this sales slip shows only $8.00? That was a $10.00 dress that girl just bought.

BOSS

ANA

4. Sandy, the "time thief."

Sandy, I told you that if I saw you fooling around one more time, I was going to fire you. Were those your friends you were just talking with?

BOSS

SANDY

5. Steve lied about his age.

Steve, the factory has a new rule. We are asking all workers to bring in a birth certificate. We have to prove that everyone working here is 18. Can you bring it in tomorrow?

BOSS

STEVE

6. Kim charged a customer too much money and kept some of it.

Kim, Mr. Blum came back for a receipt for his dinner bill. I found his bill and gave him a receipt for $20.00. But he said he paid you $21.00

BOSS

Yes, young lady. You told me the bill was $21.00 and I gave you $21.00.

CUSTOMER

KIM

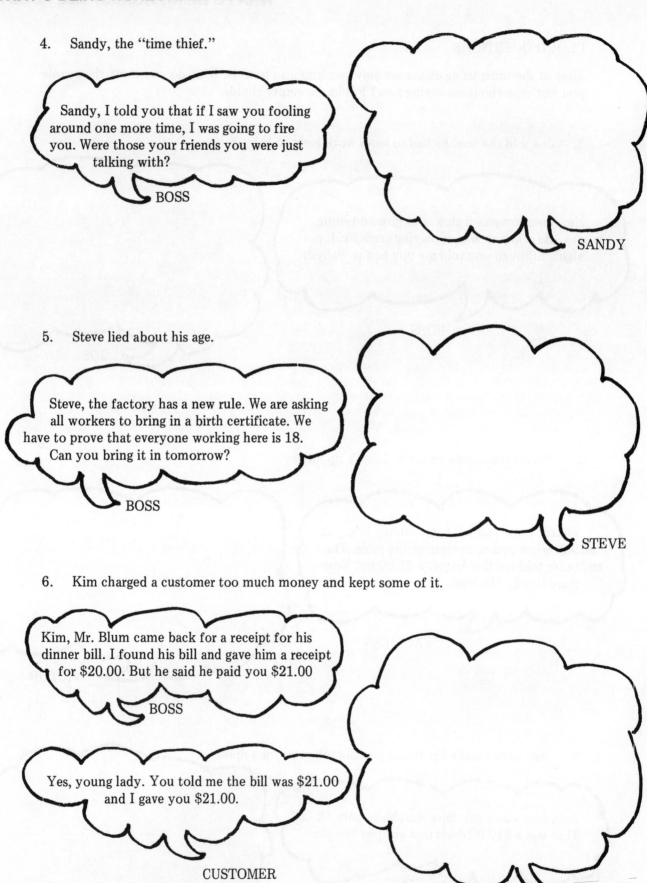

THE TRUSTOMETER

To be an honest person, you must also be trustworthy. This means that the boss can depend on you to do what you are supposed to do, even when the boss is not watching you. Where would you put each of these workers on the Trustometer? The Trustometer goes from 0 (not trustworthy) to 100 (very trustworthy).

1. Jim does not like his boss. He makes nasty wisecracks about the boss when the boss is gone. Where would you put Jim on the Trustometer?

2. Luisa tells Jim not to talk about the boss behind her back. She tells Jim to let the other workers make up their own minds about the boss. Where would you put Luisa on the Trustometer?

3. Kathy is a cook at Burger Barn. One day she burned a hamburger by mistake. She put some extra sauce on it to hide the burned part. She hoped the customer wouldn't notice. Where would you put Kathy on the Trustometer?

4. Al works at Country Cleaners. One day he broke one of the cleaning machines. Another worker told Al, "Don't tell the boss. With so many people working here, he won't know who did it." Al decided that he should tell the boss anyway. Where would you put Al on the Trustometer?

5. Tess is a stock girl at a grocery store. She is not careful when she puts things on the shelf. Sometimes a bag or jar will break and then has to be thrown away. Where would you put Tess on the Trustometer?

6. Mario gets paid an extra 15¢ an hour to keep his uniform clean. But Mario does not always wash his uniform. Sometimes when he comes to work it is dirty. Where is Mario on the Trustometer?

7. Ron is a telephone operator. He tells friends about things he hears other people say on the phone. Where would you put Ron on the Trustometer?

HOW AM I DOING AT BEING HONEST?

Now rate yourself on being honest.

Do you:	Always	Usually	Some-times	Never
1. Tell the truth? _____				
2. Admit your mistakes? _____				
3. Carefully handle money? _____				
4. Give the customer a good product? _____				
5. Charge the correct price? _____				
6. Work even when the boss isn't around? _____				
7. Try not to make excuses? _____				
8. Try not to talk behind people's backs? _____				
9. Get back to work on time after breaks? _____				
10. Pay for things you take from work? (food, clothes, equipment) _____				
11. Handle products and equipment carefully to avoid waste and damage? _____				
Now Add the Number of Checks in Each Column . . . . .TOTAL: _____				

The Rating Sheet below is for your employer to rate you on being honest. Find out if your boss is willing to do this. If so, bring the Rating Sheet or a copy of it to your boss to fill out. If the question does not apply to you, just put NA (for Not Applicable) under the column, "Always."

How is the student worker doing at being honest?

Does the Student:	Always	Usually	Some-times	Never
1. Tell the truth? _____				
2. Admit mistakes? _____				
3. Practise careful handling of money? _____				
4. Give the customer a good product? _____				
5. Charge the correct price? _____				
6. Work even when the boss isn't around? _____				
7. Try not to make excuses? _____				
8. Try not to talk behind people's backs? _____				
9. Get back to work on time after breaks? _____				
10. Pay for things taken from work? (food, clothes, equipment?) _____				
11. Handle products and equipment carefully to avoid waste and damage? _____				
Now Add the Number of Checks in Each Column . . . . TOTAL: _____				

Look at the items you or your boss have checked as "Always" or "Usually"
on page 10. Now put four of these items that show you are being honest
in the blanks below:

1. _____

2. _____

3. _____

4. _____

Pretend you are applying for a job. Using the items listed above how would you answer
the boss's questions?

I have many people applying for this job. But the
thing I am really looking for is an honest person.
How do I know that I can trust you? How do I
know if you will be an honest worker?

BOSS

YOU

HOW AM I DOING AT BEING HONEST?

"HONESTLY, THIS IS HOW IT HAPPENED . . ."

Can you think of a time when you performed
a special act of honesty or trustworthiness?
Write about it in the box below.
Use the questions to help write your story.

Who was involved?
Where were you?
How long ago did this happen?
What did happen?
How did you feel? Were you proud
of yourself?
Did anyone say anything to you
about it? What did they say?
Would you do the same thing again?

Now, using the same questions, write about a time when you were dishonest:

After writing the stories above, where would you put yourself on the honesty grid?

HONESTY GRID

	Time	Money	Products	People
I don't steal				
I don't lie				
I don't cheat				

HOW CAN I IMPROVE IN BEING HONEST?

To help you improve in being honest, keep a diary of times when you are honest or trustworthy. Write about them in the spaces below. When you're finished, show them to your teacher.

Date: _____ Place: _____

Who was there? _____

What happened? _____

How did you feel? _____

Did anyone say anything to you? If so, what? _____

_____

Would you do it again? Why/Why not? _____

_____

Date: _____ Place: _____

Who was there? _____

What happened? _____

How did you feel? _____

Did anyone say anything to you? If so, what? _____

_____

Would you do it again? Why/Why not? _____

_____

Date: _____ Place: _____

Who was there? _____

What happened? _____

How did you feel? _____

Did anyone say anything to you? If so, what? _____

_____

Would you do it again? Why/Why not? _____

_____

HOW CAN I IMPROVE IN BEING HONEST?

In sports, teams have a GAME Plan to help them win. You can have your own GAME Plan to help you improve in being honest. Sandy's GAME Plan below will help you get started. Sandy worked this GAME Plan out with her boss to improve in working when the boss was not around.

WHO?	DOES WHAT?	HOW?	WHY?	HOW DO WE KNOW?
Sandy, Sandy's boss	Sandy keeps working even when boss isn't around for next 5 working days

Start: Monday

Finish: Friday | Make a list of things to do when boss isn't around:

Clean area
Sort cartons
Restock shelves
Keep list of out-of-stock items | **+**(something good)

Sandy will get a raise

−(something bad)

Sandy will lose her job | Sandy keeps a daily record of things she did when boss wasn't around

She shows it to her boss at the end of 5 working days |

What makes your GAME Plan good?

1. Who is going to help you? _____

2. What are you trying to improve? _____

3. How are you going to do it? _____

   _____

4. What will happen to you if you do this? _____

   What will happen to you if you don't do this? _____

5. How will you know if you've reached your goal? _____

   _____

Your boss isn't always going to assist in working out a plan to help you improve on the job. She, or he, isn't always going to promise you a reward for doing things right, or let you know what bad things will happen if you don't improve.

Even so, you will find that good things do happen when you do the job right. For example, here are some of the possible good things:

You may *feel better.*
You may find the *job is easier.*
You may *get along better with the boss.*
You may *get along better with the other workers.*
You may *receive praise.*
You may *get extra things* out of the job (such as a *raise* or *promotion*).

On the other hand, if you don't do the job right, there are always bad things that happen. For example:

You may *feel lousy* on the job.
The *job may be harder* to do.
You may *get behind in your work.*
Your *boss may criticize you.*
Other *workers may criticize you.*
You may wind up *not getting a raise* or *promotion.*
You may even *get fired.*

To make your own GAME Plan, go back to page 10 and look at what you checked under the "Sometimes" and "Never" columns. Write down one thing that shows where you need to improve. This will be the DOES WHAT of your GAME Plan.

WHO?	DOES WHAT?	HOW?	WHY?	HOW DO WE KNOW?
			Think up your own idea here: **+** If I do this, I will get _____ _____ **—** If I don't do this, what will I lose? _____ _____	

2. ATTENDANCE
On the Job

WHAT'S ATTENDANCE ALL ABOUT?

One of the most important things an employer wants in a worker is good attendance. If you don't go to work, everyone else has to work harder to get the job done.

Rules for Attendance

1. You should always come to work unless you have a good reason why you are absent. This is the WHY rule.

2. If you have a good reason for being absent, then you should give your employer enough time to find someone to take your place. When you inform your employer is important. This is the WHEN rule.

3. When you call in, make sure you talk to the person in charge. Who you talk to is important. This is the WHO rule.

4. When you talk to your employer, your reason for missing work should be explained clearly and completely and given in a respectful way. How you make your explanation is important. This is the HOW rule.

Below are reasons why people miss work. Are they GOOD, OK, or POOR reasons? Check one of the boxes next to each reason to show what you think. Then ask your employer to check those he/she agrees with in the box under "Employer Agrees."

I called in and said:	Good Reason	OK, if not done often	Poor Reason	Employer Agrees
"I'm sick in bed with the flu."				
"My dad wants me to help him today."				
"My parents said I can stay home."				
"I have a cold."				
"I missed my bus."				
"My mom wants me to babysit."				
"I have a lot of homework. I can't come in today."				
"I stayed over at my friend's last night."				
"There was a death in my family. I have to go to a funeral."				
"I just don't feel good."				
"My brother came home last night. I haven't seen him in a year. He's leaving tomorrow."				
"I have no way to get to work."				
"A guy I really like asked me out tonight."				
"I have a big game on Friday. The coach said I have to practice."				
"My parents decided to go out of town today."				
"I have to go to the doctor's today."				
"I was up late last night. I'm too tired to go to work."				
"The bus passed me by at the bus stop."				
"My friend and I had a fight last night."				
I didn't call in because we don't have a phone.				

WHEN SHOULD I INFORM THE BOSS?

There are two types of reasons for missing work:
Emergencies
Special Occasions

According to the WHEN rule, you should give your employer as much notice as possible if you have to miss work.

Emergencies: Call A.S.A.P. (As Soon As Possible) — as soon as you find out you will have to miss work. You can often give your boss three hours notice or more, and the boss then has a chance to find someone to replace you.

Special Occasions: You almost always know about these long in advance. The boss expects you to give notice of this kind of absence before she or he makes up the work schedule. This is usually one or two weeks ahead of time, but check to see how much notice your employer needs.

On page 19 are some reasons why people miss work. Check one of the boxes under a or b to show WHEN you should inform your boss of your reason for missing work: A.S.A.P. (for an emergency), or 1-2 weeks (for a special occasion).

REASONS WHY PEOPLE MISS WORK

	ASAP	1-2 wks.
1. "We're going on vacation."		
2. "I have a doctor's appointment."		
3. "I'm sick in bed with the flu."		
4. "I was kept after school."		
5. "I have to help my brother move."		
6. "I want to go to the game against Central High."		
7. "I broke my leg."		
8. "I have a school field trip."		
9. "My dad said I had to stay home to help him today."		
10. "My brother came home last night. I haven't seen him in a year. He's leaving tomorrow."		
11. "I have to go to my boyfriend's graduation."		
12. "I have a dentist's appointment."		
13. "There was a death in my family. I have to go to a funeral."		
14. "I have a part in the school play."		
15. "We're going to a big concert."		
16. "My mom wants me to babysit."		
17. "I have to study for a semester exam."		
18. "I want to go on a shopping trip with my friends."		
19. "I have a date with someone I really like."		
20. "My dad was just taken to the hospital."		
21. "I have to go to my sister's wedding."		
22. "We have a family get-together."		
23. "I have to go to the prom."		

WHAT'S ATTENDANCE ALL ABOUT?

If you don't inform your employer when you are going to be absent, you will probably get fired. Giving advance notice will help you keep your job.

Read the stories below. Decide for each story whether the boss was given enough notice. If you need help, go back to page 18.

1. Marty is scheduled to come to work at 9 A.M. on Friday. He tells his employer on Thursday morning that he can't work on Friday because he has a doctor's appointment.

    Did he give enough notice? _____
    If not, when should he have told his boss? _____

2. Bill's dad came home sick one night and said, "Bill, you're going to have to call your boss and tell her I need you to run the store for me tomorrow." Bill phones his employer at 8 A.M. the next day to tell her he can't work after school.

    Did he give enough notice? _____
    If not, when should he have called in? _____

3. Sarah's grandmother died on Wednesday. Her funeral was on Friday. Sarah called her employer Friday morning to tell him that she wouldn't be in.

    Did she give enough notice? _____
    If not, when should she have told her boss? _____

4. Mike asked Maria to go out this Saturday night. "Gee, I'm supposed to work this Saturday. How about a week from Saturday?" Maria asked. Mike said okay, so Maria asked her employer for the next Saturday off.

    Did she give enough notice? _____
    If not, when should she have told her boss? _____

5. Sue is scheduled to go to work Tuesday at 6 P.M. at Floyd's Restaurant. She gets sick Tuesday morning so she stays in bed all day. She calls her employer at 5 P.M. to tell him she is sick in bed and can't come to work.

    Did she give enough notice? _____
    If not, when should she have called in? _____

6. Cindy's favorite rock star is going to be in town May 15th. She waited in line six hours to get tickets the month before. On May 12th she asked her employer for the 15th off to go to the concert. She told him she already bought the tickets.

    Did she give enough notice? _____
    If not, when should she have told her boss? _____

7. Ed's dad was hurt at work and taken to General Hospital at 2:30 P.M. on Thursday. Ed is supposed to work at 4:00 P.M. He calls at 2:45 P.M. to explain why he can't work that day.

    Did he give enough notice? _____
    If not, when should he have called in? _____

RULES OF THE ROAD

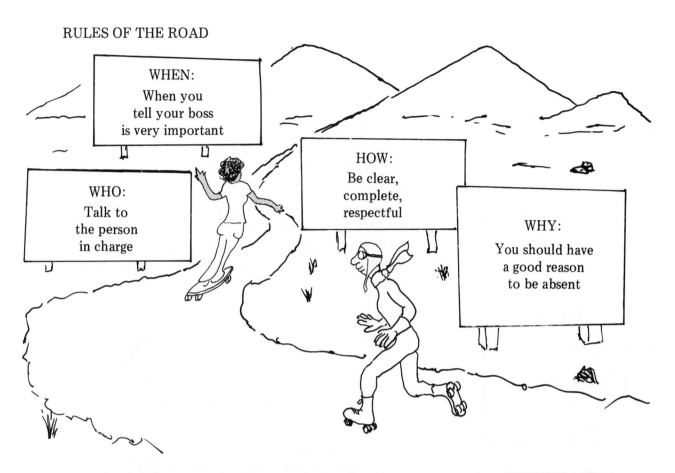

Below are telephone calls from employees to their employer. In the blank at the end of each call, describe what you would say to this employee. After that, check to see if the employee followed the above Rules of the Road for Attendance. Circle OK or not OK for WHY, WHEN, WHO and HOW.

1. Mary starts work at 3 P.M. She was sick all night with a cold and a fever. She calls her employer at 8 A.M. and Roberto, another worker, answers the phone:

    Mary: "May I speak to Mrs. Jones? This is Mary."

    Roberto: "Mrs. Jones isn't here, yet. She'll be in at 8:30."

    Mary: "That's all right. Tell her I was sick all night with a cold and fever. I can't come in today."

    Roberto: "You'd better call back and talk to Mrs. Jones."

WHY: OK Not OK   WHEN: OK Not OK   WHO: OK Not OK   HOW: OK Not OK

WHAT'S ATTENDANCE ALL ABOUT?

2. Eva is due at work at 10 A.M. Eva's mother works during the week and always goes shopping on Saturdays. She usually drops Eva's baby sister off at the babysitter's. Today, the babysitter had to go away. Her mother tells Eva that she can't go to work today. She has to stay home and take care of her little sister. Eva calls her boss at 8:30 A.M.

Eva: "May I speak to Mr. Morales?"

Employer: "This is Mr. Morales."

Eva: "I'm sorry, Mr. Morales. I can't come to work today. My mother had to go shopping and I have to watch my sister."

Employer: "What do you mean, you have to watch your sister? Doesn't your mother know you have a job? I need you here."

Eva: "I'm awfully sory. I don't want to stay home. My mom is making me. Usually, the babysitter is home on Saturday. She had to go away today. My mom works all week. Today is the only day she has to shop."

Employer: _____

| WHY: OK Not OK |
| WHEN: OK Not OK |
| WHO: OK Not OK |
| HOW: OK Not OK |

KEEP ON
TRUCKIN'

3. Donna begins work at 11 A.M. Her friends come over on Saturday morning. She is having fun and doesn't want to go to work. Everyone is talking about going swimming later on. Donna calls in at 10 A.M. and Mr. Ying, the employer, answers the phone:

Donna: "Mr. Ying, this is Donna. A group of my friends came over this morning. I hardly ever see them except at school. We're planning a party and we all want to go swimming this afternoon. Is it okay if I don't go to work today?"

Employer: "You know it's Saturday. We're going to have a busy day, Donna."

Donna: "Well, I'm always there. I worked last night. I'll work tomorrow if you want me."

Employer: "But I need you today."

Donna: "Yes, but I can only see my friends on Saturday, you know. This is special."

Employer: _____

_____

| WHY: OK Not OK | WHEN: OK Not OK | WHO: OK Not OK | HOW: OK Not OK |

4. Marsha's brother has flown in from California and is on his way to Boston. He is staying over at the airport for three hours. He called Marsha and asked her to visit him at the airport. Marsha is due to start at Woodstock Cleaners in four hours. She calls her employer, and Shirley, another worker, answers the phone.

    Marsha: "Is Mrs. Toohey in? This is Marsha."

    Shirley: "No, but she said she'll be back in five minutes. Why don't you call then? She really needs you today."

    Marsha: "Shirley, I'm in a big hurry. Tell Mrs. Toohey I won't be in today. Something important's come up, okay?"

    Shirley: _____

              _____

WHY: OK Not OK	WHEN: OK Not OK	WHO: OK Not OK	HOW: OK Not OK

5. Ramon is expected at work by 11. His uncle came over this morning. He asked Ramon if he'd like to go to the football game with him. Ramon wants to go. He calls in at 9 A.M.

    Ramon: "May I speak to Mr. Aronson?"

    Employer: "This is Mr. Aronson."

    Ramon: "Is it okay if I don't come to work today? My uncle brought me tickets to the football game today and I want to go. He asked me if I would like to go with him. Maybe I could work just during the rush hour."

    Employer: "Well, Ramon, I really wanted you for the whole day. If you'd have called earlier, I could have gotten someone to take your place. What time is the game?"

    Ramon: "It starts at 1:30."

    Employer: "Could you come in from 11 A.M. to 1 P.M.?"

    Ramon: "I have to be there at 1. Could I work from 10 to 12:30?"

    Employer: _____

               _____

WHY: OK Not OK	WHEN: OK Not OK	WHO: OK Not OK	HOW: OK Not OK

23

HOW AM I DOING IN ATTENDANCE?

MISSING PERSONS CHECKLIST

How well are you doing at attendance on the job? Read each sentence and check the one that best shows your attendance at work.

_____ I never miss work. (4000 points)

_____ I hardly ever miss work. (3000 points)

_____ I miss work sometimes. (2000 points)

_____ I miss work often. (1000 points)

_____ I'm hardly ever at work. (0 points)

How strong are you in attendance? Can you ring the attendance bell?
In the picture below, mark how many points you have scored.

WHY DO I MISS WORK?

Do you miss work a lot?
Check your reasons below.

I miss work because

_____ 1. I am sick a lot.

_____ 2. I don't like the job.

_____ 3. I don't like the boss.

_____ 4. I have to babysit.

_____ 5. I'm out for sports.

_____ 6. I have problems at home.

_____ 7. I am bored with the job.

_____ 8. I'm not very good at my job.

_____ 9. My boss doesn't like me.

_____ 10. I have a lot of homework to do.

_____ 11. I have trouble getting to work.

_____ 12. I have too many other things to do.

_____ 13. I don't like the people I work with.

_____ 14. I have trouble getting up in the morning.

_____ 15. My parents don't want me to work.

_____ 16. I want to be with my friends who are not working.

_____ 17. I have many jobs to do at home that keep me from going to work.

_____ 18. I really don't know why I miss so much.

_____ 19. Other. Write out your reason. _____

_____

_____

HOW CAN I IMPROVE IN ATTENDANCE?

Here is a GAME PLAN that shows how Dwight, his boss, and another worker helped Dwight improve in attendance. Below it is a GAME Plan for you to fill in.

WHO?	DOES WHAT?	HOW?	WHY?	HOW DO WE KNOW?
Dwight, boss, another worker	Dwight comes to work by 8:30 A.M. every day for 2 weeks Start: Feb. 1 Finish: Feb. 14	Dwight asks another worker to call at 7:30 A.M. every other day to make sure he is up	**+** Dwight will be allowed to work 5 extra hours (5 hrs. X $5.25 per hr. = $26.25) **—** Dwight will lose his job	Dwight, his boss, and the other worker will check his timecard at at the end of each week

WHO?	DOES WHAT?	HOW?	WHY?	HOW DO WE KNOW?
			+ If I do this, I will get _____ _____ **—** If I don't do this, what will I lose? _____ _____	

Before you fill in this GAME Plan, review pages 14 and 15 in Chapter 1.

3. WILLINGNESS TO WORK
On the Job

WHAT'S WILLINGNESS TO WORK ALL ABOUT?

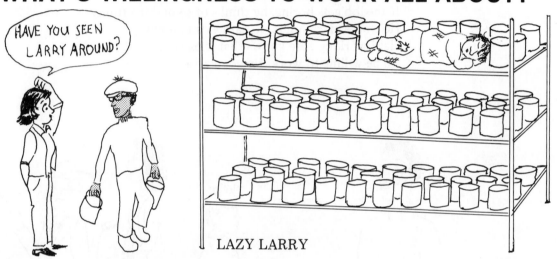

LAZY LARRY

Lazy Larry has to change his ways.
He likes to swim on sunny days.
So he went to work when he wanted to.
Sometimes he called in and said he had the flu.
When he came to work he would fool around.
When it was time to clean, Larry couldn't be found.
He was never cheerful, just always complained.
His uniform was always stained.
He thought his job was an awful bore.
He would put in his time, but nothing more.
He would oversleep and come to work late.
He often made the customers wait.
Lazy Larry was too tired one day. . .
Lazy Larry got fired one day.

1. Underline the things in the poem that tell you that Larry was not willing to work.

2. If you were the boss, would you have fired Larry? _____

3. What do you think Larry will do now? _____

4. Can you think of any other ways that show *poor* willingness to work? List them.

_____   _____

_____   _____

HARD — WORKING JOSÉ

Hard-working José works hard each day.
He likes his job and earns his pay.
While others stand around when business gets slow,
He does extra work to make the time go.
The customers like him, because he is kind.
When asked to work overtime, he says, "I don't mind."
He offers ideas to do the job better.
His co-workers think he's a real go-getter.
He helps them with their work when he has the time.
He never says, "That job is not mine."
If the job gets boring, he thinks of something funny.
He works extra hours, to earn extra money.
Hard-working José knows that it pays
To be willing to work. He got a raise.

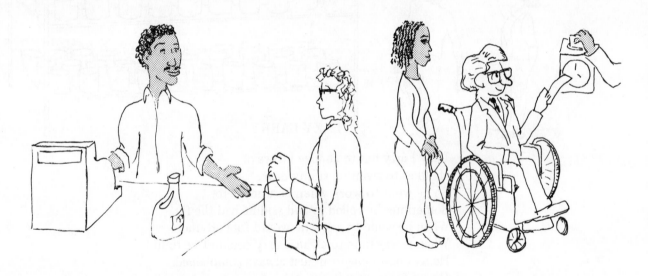

1. Underline the things in the poem that show José's willingness to work.

2. Do you think that José is a good worker? _____

3. Do you think that José deserved a raise? _____ Why or why not?

    _____

4. What do you think will happen to José in the future? _____

    _____

5. Can you think of any other ways that show good willingness to work? List them.

    _____   _____

    _____   _____

BRIDGING BOREDOM

Many people get bored with their jobs at times.
But there are things you can do to keep from
getting bored. Take a survey of at least five people
(try to ask one parent, one teacher, one employer
and two other workers). Find out what each one
does to keep from getting bored on the job. Write
the results of your survey on the Bridge Over
Boring Waters.

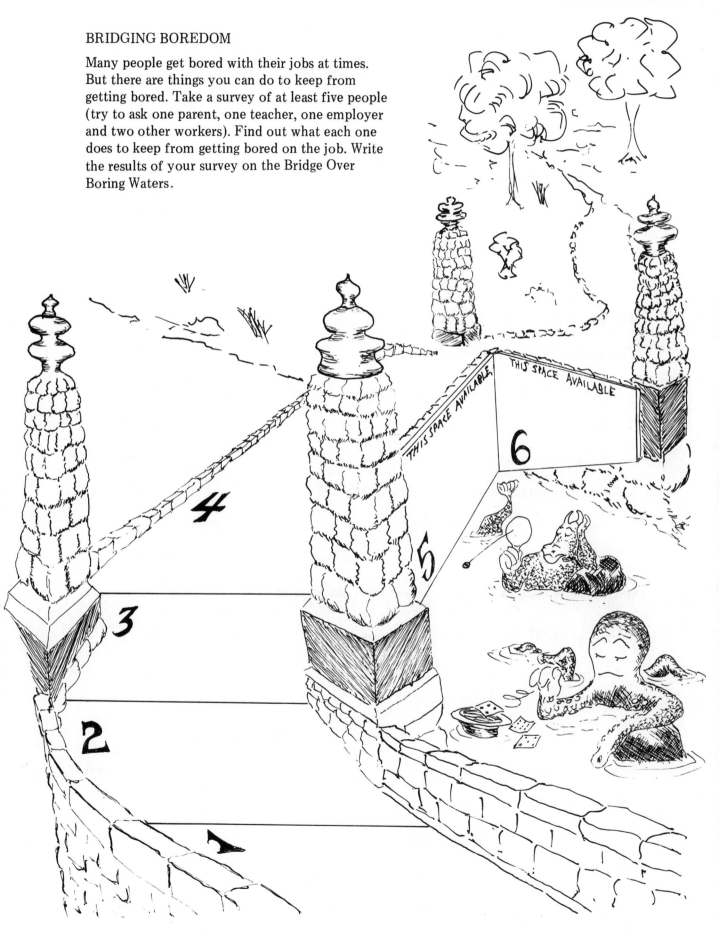

WHAT'S WILLINGNESS TO WORK ALL ABOUT?

IF YOUR JOB'S A BOWL OF CHERRIES, WHAT DO YOU DO ABOUT THE PITS?

Interview someone who likes her/his job. Find out what that person does about the parts she/he doesn't like. Here are some questions you might ask.

_____   _____
              Name   Occupation

Why do you like your job?

    1. _____

    2. _____

    3. _____

How long have you had your job? _____

What are some of your job duties?

    1. _____   4. _____

    2. _____   5. _____

    3. _____   6. _____

Is there anything that you don't like about the job? What?

    _____ _____

_____

Has there ever been a time when you didn't feel like going to work? _____

What did you do? _____

_____

Make up some questions of your own.

Q. _____

    A. _____

Q. _____

    A. _____

Q. _____

    A. _____

WORKING YOUR WAY UP

Most people begin working in *entry-level* jobs. They start out in jobs that older people with skills would not do. You will probably have to start at the bottom, but this does not mean that you have to quit in order to get a better job. Many jobs offer you the chance to work your way up, *if* you are willing to start at the bottom and stick with the job. Then the boss will know that you are a good worker and may give you a *promotion*. The diagrams below show how you can work your way up from different entry-level jobs.

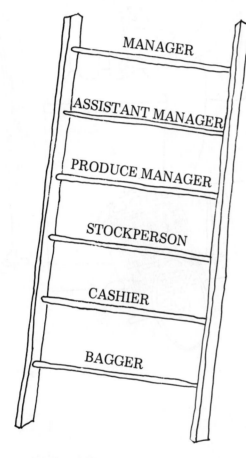

MANAGER

ASSISTANT MANAGER

PRODUCE MANAGER

STOCKPERSON

CASHIER

BAGGER

MANAGER

ASSISTANT MANAGER

HEAD CHEF

COOK

BUSPERSON

DISHWASHER

MANAGER

FLOOR MANAGER

SALESPERSON

CASHIER

MAINTENANCE

Fill in how you could move up in your job.

31

WHAT'S WILLINGNESS TO WORK ALL ABOUT?

MOVING UP IN THE WORLD

Mrs. Peters manages a company which has an opening for an assistant manager. She would like to promote one of the workers below. If you were Mrs. Peters, which worker would you move up?

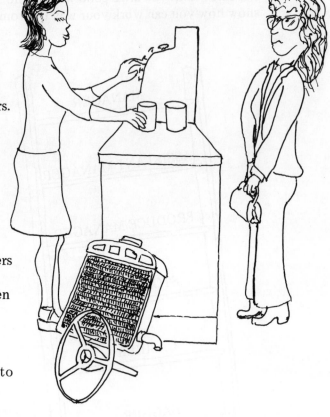

Nida Santiago:

Has been with the company for two years. Often late because her car keeps breaking down. Works overtime when asked. Is friendly to the customers.

Peter van Donk:

Works hard and helps other workers with their jobs. Often his friends stop by work to see him. Came to work with a hangover one day.

Leonard Lief:

Good attendance at work. Is friendly to customers and other workers. Talks and fools around with other workers. Sometimes smokes on the job even though it isn't allowed.

Roscoe Brown:

Is helpful to other workers and customers. Asks to work extra hours. Has good attendance at work. Has been late four times in the past six months.

Lanese Williams:

Always comes to work when she is supposed to and even asks for extra hours. Her uniform is dirty sometimes. Smiles and says "thank you" to the customers.

Which worker would you promote? _____

Why? _____

_____

HOW AM I DOING AT WILLINGNESS TO WORK?

Interview yourself about your own job. When you are finished, you might want to make a class scrapbook or bulletin board.

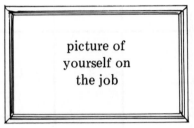

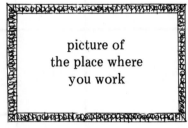

Name:

Place of employment:

Job title:

Number of days per week I work:

Name of employer:

Names of other workers:

Things I like about my job:

Things I do well at my job:

Things I don't like about my job:

Things I need to improve in on my job:

The good things I get out of my job:

WILLINGNESS TO WORK PROFILE

Here is a profile which will tell you about your willingness to work. Take this to your employer. Ask him/her to circle the numbers that show your willingness to work.

Excellent	5	5	5	5	5	5	5
Good	4	4	4	4	4	4	4
Satisfactory	3	3	3	3	3	3	3
Needs Improvement	2	2	2	2	2	2	2
Danger Of Being Fired	1	1	1	1	1	1	1
	Helps Others	Does Work Willingly	Does Assigned Tasks	Willing to Work Extra Hours When Needed	Doesn't Miss Work	Offers Helpful Ideas	Does Extra Work

Add up all the circled numbers. What is your total score? _____

WORKER OF THE MONTH CLUB

Each month you can put up the name and picture of the worker who has scored the highest on the Willingness To Work Profile. If you don't make it to the top this month, find out where you can improve on your Profile so you can make it to the top next month.

HOW CAN I IMPROVE IN WILLINGNESS TO WORK?

Your Interview of yourself, and your Willingness to Work Profile tell you where you can improve in willingness. You can use a GAME Plan to help you do better. Read the plan Burt and his boss worked out. Then make a GAME Plan of your own.

WHO?	DOES WHAT?	HOW?	WHY?	HOW DO WE KNOW?
Burt, his boss	Burt won't gripe when asked to work in stockroom for 10 working days Start: Oct. 3 Finish: Oct. 17	Burt puts a note inside his locker at work to remind him of this	**+** Burt's boss will stop being angry with him **−** Burt will not get promoted	Burt will check with the boss every other day to see if he has griped

If you need a reminder on how to set up your GAME Plan, go back to pages 14 and 15.

WHO?	DOES WHAT?	HOW?	WHY?	HOW DO WE KNOW?

4. ACCEPTING ORDERS
On the Job

WHAT'S ACCEPTING ORDERS ALL ABOUT?

All workers have to accept orders. This is part of the job. Rhea didn't like to accept orders until she found out why the boss has the right to give orders.

RHEA, I WANT YOU TO MOP THIS FLOOR RIGHT AWAY!

WHO DOES SHE THINK SHE IS? WHAT RIGHT DOES SHE HAVE TO ORDER ME AROUND?

DO YOU REALLY WANT TO KNOW? IF THE BOSS DOESN'T GIVE THE ORDERS, IMPORTANT THINGS DON'T GET DONE...

WHO SAID ANYTHING ABOUT KEYS?

IF SOMETHING BREAKS DOWN, THE BOSS IS RESPONSIBLE FOR MAKING SURE IT GETS FIXED.

THE BOSS IS EVEN RESPONSIBLE FOR MAKING SURE EVERYONE GETS PAID.

DON'T YOU THINK THE BOSS HAS THE RIGHT TO GIVE ORDERS?

I GET THE POINT.

DIFFERENT KINDS OF BOSSES

Bosses come in all shapes and sizes. They all have their own ways of giving orders. Here are some different kinds of bosses.

THE MIXED—UP BOSS

The Mixed-Up boss gets upset and confused, sometimes giving orders that you can't understand. This boss may get even more mixed up if a lot of customers are waiting. So what can you do? If the Mixed-Up boss is not busy, say that you didn't understand the orders. If the boss is busy, ask one of the other workers what you should do.

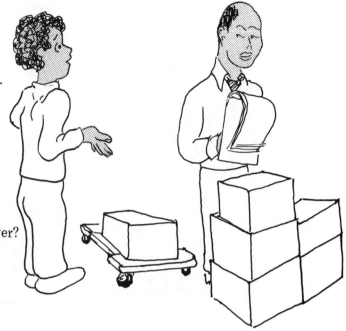

How mixed up does your boss get?
Is the boss mixed up all the time? Sometimes? Never?
Rate your boss below.
(0 = never mixed up; 10 = mixed up all the time.)

THE BARKER

The Barker gives orders in a loud voice and sounds rough, barking even louder when it gets busy. Some workers think that the Barker doesn't like them when he or she yells at them. But talking loudly is just the way this boss gets things done. The best thing to do if you work for a Barker is to do what you are told and don't bark back. If you need to talk to the boss, do it when things aren't busy.

Rate your boss on the Barkometer. How loud does your boss give orders? Draw an arrow to where your boss would be.

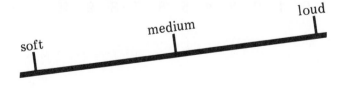

soft   medium   loud

THE DOUBLE BOSS

Some workers have more than one boss. Two or more bosses giving orders is not likely to double your pleasure, double your fun. Sometimes one boss will tell a worker to do one thing and the other boss will tell the worker to do something else. Then the worker doesn't know what to do. If you work for a double boss and each one gives you a different order, you should:

Tell one boss what the other boss told you to do.

Ask the boss which of the two things you should do.

Talk to both bosses together, when things calm down.

How many people give you orders at work? Circle the number of heads.

1 2 3 4 5 6 7

THE QUIET BOSS

The Quiet boss doesn't talk much. Even if you do a great job, this type of boss is not likely to compliment you. If you have a quiet boss, you may think she or he doesn't like you, just because this boss doesn't talk much. Or you may find yourself wondering if you are doing a good job. If you work for the Quiet boss, ask the boss if you are doing a good job. That might help the Quiet boss to start talking to you.

How quiet is your boss?
Rate your boss on the Quietometer below.
Draw an arrow to where your boss would be.

not so quiet	quiet	super quiet

THE COMPLAINER BOSS

The Complainer boss never seems to be happy with what employees do. This boss always finds something that isn't done right. All bosses complain sometimes. The Complainer boss complains all the time.

How does your boss rate in the complaint department?   Does your boss complain a little? Sometimes? A lot?
Put an X under the picture that shows your boss.

COMPLAINT DEPARTMENT

THE NICE BOSS

This boss gives orders in a nice way. If you forget, or make a mistake, the nice boss will tell you what to do again. This will help you learn the right way to do things.

How nice is your boss?
Does your boss have a big heart?
Rate your boss on the scale below.

0 1 2 3 4 5 6 7 8 9 10

DIFFERENT BOSSES IN REVIEW

Here are some problems with the different kinds of bosses. Circle the best answer for each problem.

1. The restaurant where you work is getting very busy. Hungry customers are waiting for their food. The Barker yells at you to make some coffee. You should:

    a) Yell back at the boss loudly, "OK!"

    b) Say, "All right," and make the coffee.

    c) Make the coffee very slowly so the boss will know that you don't like being yelled at.

    Which answer did you choose? _____ Why? _____

    _____

2. You work in a paint store, and you have just finished putting away some of the paint that was delivered today. The Complainer says that you put some things in the wrong places. You should:

    a) Ask where the right place is for these cans.

    b) Walk away without saying anything.

    c) Give your boss a dirty look.

    Which answer did you choose? _____ Why? _____

    _____

3. Your boss, the Quiet One, never says much to you. You wish the boss would tell you if you are doing a good job. You should:

    a) Write the boss a note asking if you are doing a good job.

    b) Threaten to quit.

    c) Ask the boss if you have been doing a good job.

    Which answer did you choose? _____ Why? _____

    _____

4. Your boss is the Mixed-Up one. You work in an apartment building. When you came to work you were told to sweep the hall. The boss sees you sweeping the hall and asks you to mow the lawn right away. You should:

   a) Say, "Make up your mind."

   b) Keep on sweeping.

   c) Ask, "Which job do you want me to finish first?"

   Which answer did you choose? _____ Why? _____

   _____

5. Your boss asks you to help a new employee. You should:

   a) Say, "I will when I get time."

   b) Do what the boss says right away.

   c) Tell the boss it's not your job.

   Which answer did you choose? _____ Why? _____

   _____

6. The grocery store where you work has more than one boss. The manager tells you to collect the grocery carts. Another boss comes out and tells you to bag groceries. You should:

   a) Do what the first boss tells you.

   b) Do what the second boss tells you.

   c) Tell the boss that the manager told you to collect the carts. Ask which you should do.

   Which answer did you choose? _____ Why? _____

   _____

7. The Nice boss tells you that you wrote up a sales slip the wrong way. Then the boss shows you how to do it. You should:

   a) Explain why your way makes sense.

   b) Thank the boss for helping you learn the right way.

   c) Say, "I'm new here. If you don't like the way I work, maybe you should hire someone else."

   Which answer did you choose? _____ Why? _____

   _____

AN INTERVIEW WITH YOUR BOSS

Your boss (also called your *supervisor*) has many duties you may not know about. Find out if your boss is willing to answer questions from you about what a supervisor's job is like. Use the questions below, and write down the answers as your boss talks. If your boss is too busy for an interview, try to answer the questions yourself. Imagine that you are the boss. Either way, the interview will help you understand what work is like for your boss.

INTERVIEW FORM

Company _____ Type of Business _____

Supervisor's Name _____ Supervisor's Title _____

1. How many hours do you work each week? _____

2. What time do you get to work in the morning? _____

3. What time do you go home in the evening? _____

4. Do *you* have a boss? _____

5. What are your most important duties as boss? _____

6. What was the worst thing that ever happened to you as a boss? _____

    _____

7. When customers get mad, what do you do to make them feel better? _____

    _____

8. What are the hardest things about being a boss? _____

    _____

9. What special training did you need to become the boss? _____

    _____

Date _____ Signature of Supervisor _____

WHAT'S ACCEPTING ORDERS ALL ABOUT?

ACCEPTING ORDERS: WHAT SHOULD I SAY?

When the boss gives you an order, you should always give an answer. This will let the boss know that you are going to accept the order. If you accept orders willingly, the boss will know that you are a good worker. This doesn't mean that you have to do a handstand. But don't just stand there like a big blob, either.

There are two ways that you can accept an order:

By what you *say* (your words)
By what you *do* (your actions)

Below is a tic-tac-toe game. It shows things that you should say and should not say when your boss gives you an order. You will be X. Put an X in the spaces that tell the right way to accept orders. Put an O in the spaces that tell the wrong way to accept orders. See if you can win!

No way!	Why me?	Sure
All right	How come?	Not again!
Right away	Yes, certainly	Okay

ACCEPTING ORDERS: WHAT SHOULD I DO?

People can say things without talking.

They can say things with their eyes.

They can say things with their mouths.

They can say things with their bodies.

Below are some things that people are saying with their eyes. Draw a line from the eyes to what you think they are saying.

I am very mad   I don't know what to do   I am bored

Here are some things that people are saying with their mouths. Draw a line from each mouth to what you think it is saying.

I am happy   I don't like that   I am sad

Below are some things that people are saying with their bodies. Draw a line from each body to what you think it is saying.

I hope no one sees me
sneaking by

I am sad   You are late

WHAT'S ACCEPTING ORDERS ALL ABOUT?

Let's see if you can tell the right way to accept an order without talking. Check the picture that shows how a good worker would look.

Your boss tells you to take out the garbage. You like your job, but you don't like to take out the garbage. How should you accept this order?

The boss just yelled at you to work faster. How should you accept this order?

44

The boss tells you that it is your turn to do a job that no one in your office likes to do, but everyone has to take turns at. How should you accept this order?

A customer complained because her grocery bag broke. The boss says that you did not bag her groceries the right way. She tells you to do it over. How should you accept this order?

HOW AM I DOING AT ACCEPTING ORDERS?

Read the answers below. Check the answers that *you* give to your boss when you are told to do something at work.

_____ "OK"

_____ "Me again?"

_____ "I suppose so."

_____ "All right."

_____ "Yes, certainly."

_____ "Sure."

_____ "How come I always have to do that?"

_____ "If I have time."

_____ "Work, work, work! That's all I do."

_____ "Right away."

_____ "I'm tired of this place."

_____ "What for?"

_____ "Boy, I'm always getting yelled at."

CHECK YOUR A.Q. (Acceptance Quotient)

Check the boxes that tell how you accept orders. Then ask your boss to answer the questions too.

How Do I Accept Orders?	Always	Usually	Sometimes	Hardly Ever
Do I smile?				
Does this worker smile?				
Do I give a positive response?				
Does this worker give a positive response?				
Do I do the job right away?				
Does this worker do the job right away?				
TOTAL				

HOW CAN I IMPROVE AT ACCEPTING ORDERS?

There are three things that a good worker should do when the boss gives an order. These things show the *right* way to accept orders. Practice these things every day to help you to improve your A.Q. (acceptance quotient).

> *Smile.*
> Give a *positive response* (such as "I'll be happy to," "yes," etc.)
> Do what the boss asks *right away*.

Read these stories about workers accepting orders. Then answer the questions in the chart below.

1. The boss asked Tom to help unload the truck. "Why me?" Tom grumbled, and he slowly walked over to the truck.
2. Aurelia was asked to wash the dishes at work. She smiled and said, "Okay." Then she started the dishes right away.
3. Judy was asked to help some customers. "Sure," she said with a smile. On the way, she stopped to talk with some other workers.
4. "I want you to clean up the toy section," the store manager said. Marcos smiled and started to do the job.
5. Beth works at a Day Care Center. Her boss asked her to read the children a story. "All right," she said with a frown, and began to read the story.

	Smile?	Give a positive response?	Do the job right away?
1. Did Tom. . . .			
2. Did Aurelia. . . .			
3. Did Judy. . . .			
4. Did Marcos. . . .			
5. Did Beth. . . .			

Which worker accepts orders the best? _____

Which worker is the worst? _____

HOW CAN I IMPROVE AT ACCEPTING ORDERS?

Here is a partly finished GAME Plan that is *guaranteed* to help you improve in Accepting Orders. Fill in the rest of the GAME Plan. Then use it and see if your boss notices!

WHO?	DOES WHAT?	HOW?	WHY?	HOW DO WE KNOW
	Will try to improve at accepting orders days. Start: Finish:	Each time my boss gives me an order, I will: smile give a positive response do the job right away		

48

5. GETTING ALONG WITH OTHERS
On the Job

WHAT'S GETTING ALONG WITH OTHERS ALL ABOUT?

The Rotten Rockers band sounds terrible. They can't get along with each other on the job. There are six people in the band:

DRUMMER	PIANO PLAYER	GUITAR PLAYER
SINGER	HORN PLAYER	TAMBOURINE PLAYER

Each one has a special way of *not* getting along with the others. Which player does each of the things below?

Puts others down _____   Complains _____

Gossips _____   Is not helpful _____

Is bossy _____   Fights _____

Now you know why the Rotten Rockers sound so bad. Keep reading to find out what getting along with others on the job is all about.

WHAT'S GETTING ALONG WITH OTHERS ALL ABOUT?

HELPING OTHERS ON THE JOB

Workers help each other in different ways. Choose at least four people you know who work at the jobs listed below. (Each one should have a different job.) Ask each one, "How do you help the people you work with?" Write what they say in the boxes below.

AUTO MECHANIC	YOUR BOSS
BUS DRIVER	POLICE OFFICER
CONSTRUCTION WORKER	RESTAURANT WORKER
OFFICE WORKER	WORKER IN A STORE
FACTORY WORKER	TEACHER
FARM WORKER	TRUCK DRIVER

What are some ways you could be helpful to other workers on your job?

1. _____

2. _____

3. _____

50

JUNKING THOSE BOSSY WORDS

Below are bossy ways of asking for help on the job. Bossy ways of asking for things need to be junked! Write each sentence in a way that is *not* bossy.

1. Get me a roll of dimes.   _____

2. Take that order.   _____

3. You're in my way.   _____

4. Give me that paper.   _____

5. How many times do I have to tell you to
   shut up?   _____

6. You're bugging me. Get lost.   _____

7. Do it the way I told you.   _____

8. You're too slow.   _____

9. Won't you ever learn?   _____

10. I can't hear. Shut up.   _____

11. Clean your ears out. I already told you once. _____

12. Get moving.   _____

13. Hey you, answer that phone.   _____

     Do you know someone at work who is bossy? _____

     Do you like that person?_____

     Why or why not?_____

WHAT'S GETTING ALONG WITH OTHERS ALL ABOUT?

AGREEABLE WORKERS

Are you an agreeable worker? If you are, you get along at work. You don't fight, complain, or argue with other workers. The pictures and stories below tell about people who are *not* agreeable. Next to each story, fill in what an AGREEABLE person would have said. Then draw what the AGREEABLE person might look like.

FIGHTING FAY	FRIENDLY FILOMENA	ARGUING ARNOLD	AGREEABLE AHMED
Fighting Fay was on break. Another worker, George accidentally bumped her. He said, "I'm sorry." But she pushed him and snapped, "Watch it next time!"	What would Friendly Filomena have said to George?	Arguing Arnold's boss told him to work a little faster. Arnold argued, "How can I work any faster? I'm already working fast."	What would Agreeable Ahmed have said to his boss?
COMPLAINING CAL	BRIGHT-SIDE BERNIE	GROUCHY GLENDA	HAPPY HARRIET
Complaining Cal works in a restaurant. At lunch hour he complained, "Where are all these people coming from? I've had it with these crowds."	What would Bright-side Bernie say to Cal?	Grouchy Glenda is always mad. She never smiles or says "Hi." When Jean said to her, "How are you doing today?" Glenda grouched, "What's it to you?"	What would Happy Harriet have said?

Which of the workers above are *you* like? (You can pick more than one.)

_____

What do *you* do that *they* do? _____

52

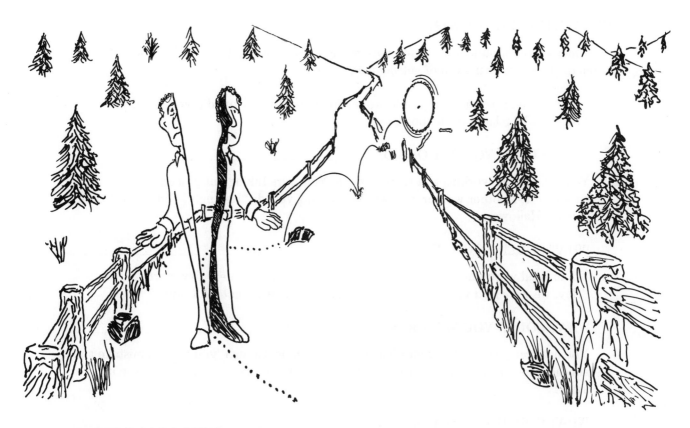

PAINFUL PUT-DOWNS

A put-down can make you feel like you've gone through a buzz-saw. Think of some of the put-downs you have heard. Write them in the road above.

To answer the questions below, describe what has happened at work. If you don't have a job right now, describe a put-down about working on homework, a chore at home, or some other job.

1. What happened the last time you got put down? _____

    _____

    _____

2. How did it make you feel? _____

3. Do you like that person? _____

4. What happened the last time you put someone else down? _____

    _____

    _____

5. How do you think it made that person feel? _____

6. Do you think that person likes you? _____

THOSE PUT-DOWNS AT WORK

Sometimes a worker puts down other workers just to see them get mad. What could you do in each of these stories instead of getting mad?

1. You dropped a garbage bag and it broke. Someone said, "How did you get hired? You must be related to the boss."

    WHAT COULD YOU SAY OR DO? _____

2. You just started working at a grocery store. You were taking out groceries to the parking lot. Another worker who was just leaving yelled, "Hey ugly! Did you get that face for Halloween?"

    WHAT COULD YOU SAY OR DO? _____

3. You missed work one day because you had a bad cold. The next day, a worker said, "Hey, we were glad you weren't here yesterday. We really got a lot done."

    WHAT COULD YOU SAY OR DO? _____

4. You are pretty good at making change. This morning, though, you made a mistake and another worker said, "You're supposed to collect the money, dummy, not give it away!"

    WHAT COULD YOU SAY OR DO? _____

OTHERS HEAR PUT DOWNS TOO!

In story #3 above, a worker said, "Hey, we were glad you weren't here yesterday. We really got a lot done."

A customer, the boss, and other workers all heard the put-down.

What do you think the customer might think, do, or say? _____

_____

What do you think the boss might think, do, or say?

_____

_____

What do you think other workers might think, do, or say? _____

_____

You can't buy this spray in a store. But you can get rid of put-downs if you can
LAUGH it off,
TALK to your boss,
IGNORE it,
REMIND yourself that
PUT-DOWNS ARE FOR PUNKS.

ACCEPTING CRITICISM

Criticism does not have to be a bad thing. Criticism can be a suggestion for improvement. Criticism can help you be better at your job. Read the stories below. What will happen to each worker if the boss does not make a suggestion for improvement?

1. Bill talks on the phone a lot at work. He also takes long lunch hours. Other workers see that. WHAT WILL HAPPEN TO BILL IF HIS BOSS DOESN'T CRITICIZE HIM?

_____

_____

2. Lena often forgets to punch out from work. Sometimes her boss is not sure how many hours she has worked. WHAT WILL HAPPEN TO LENA IF HER BOSS DOES NOT CRITICIZE HER?

_____

_____

3. Jake is a very good worker. On Tuesday, he was sick. He forgot to call in to work. WHAT WILL HAPPEN TO JAKE IF HIS BOSS DOESN'T CRITICIZE HIM?

_____

4. Ellie works in a restaurant. Her writing is very hard to read. Sometimes the cook can't read her orders. WHAT WILL HAPPEN TO ELLIE IF SOMEONE DOESN'T CRITICIZE HER?

_____

5. Geraldo gets paid for how much he sells. He takes long breaks and comes to work late. WHAT WILL HAPPEN TO GERALDO IF HIS BOSS DOESN'T CRITICIZE HIM?

_____

Now you can see how criticism can help. Some people do not take criticism well. Some workers:

> BLAME SOMEONE ELSE — "It's Pete's fault."
> ARGUE THAT IT'S NOT THEIR FAULT — "I did not do it wrong."
> MAKE EXCUSES — "If this cash register was any good, I'd be faster."
> COMPLAIN ABOUT BEING PICKED ON — "You always get mad at *me*."
> POUT — (Won't talk at all.)

Do you do any of those things when you are criticized at work? If so, put a check (√) by it. That is something you need to stop doing.

WHAT'S GETTING ALONG WITH OTHERS ALL ABOUT?

THEY COULDN'T ACCEPT CRITICISM

Read each story below. Then decide how each worker acted when criticized. Each person either:

BLAMED SOMEONE ELSE

or

ARGUED THAT IT WAS NOT HIS OR HER FAULT

or

MADE EXCUSES   or   POUTED

or

COMPLAINED ABOUT BEING PICKED ON

Write how each person acted in the upper right corner of each card below. The first one is done for you.

made excuses

Lorne said, "I would have swept the floor last night, but I couldn't find a broom."

A worker said to Carla, "When you were late today, I had to do your job and mine too." Carla said, "Why does everyone always pick on me?"

Tomiko did not come to work Friday night. She told her boss, "Michael was supposed to call me to tell me my schedule. But he never called."

Linda's boss told her she wrote the wrong phone message down. Linda said, "I wrote down just what the person said. I know I wrote it down all right."

Juan's boss told him he should be more friendly to the customers. Juan went into the back room and sat by himself.

Below are some good ways to accept criticism. Write the name of a person from each story in the cards beside the answer he or she *should have* given.

1. "Thanks for telling me. I'll listen more carefully next time." _____

2. "It's hard for me to talk to strangers. But I'll try harder." _____

3. "I should have checked my schedule myself. I'll do it this week." _____

4. "I'm sorry about that. I'll make sure it doesn't happen again." _____

5. "You're right. I guess I didn't look for that broom very hard." _____

GOSSIP AND TRUST DON'T MIX

Can other workers trust you? You can be trusted by co-workers if you:

Don't spread gossip

Stand up for co-workers
when others talk behind their backs.

Below are stories about gossip. Circle the answers that show you can be trusted.

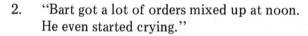

1. "Did you hear that Rita gave back too much change to a customer?"

   YOU COULD SAY:
   A. She is so slow.
   B. That figures. She flunked math.
   C. It was probably her friend and they are going to split up.
   D. I'm sure she didn't mean to.

2. "Bart got a lot of orders mixed up at noon. He even started crying."

   YOU COULD SAY:
   A. He's always been a crybaby.
   B. I'll ask him if he needs a Kleenex
   C. Wait till his girlfriend hears about this!
   D. He must have really been upset. Let's help him next time it gets busy.

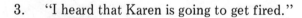

3. "I heard that Karen is going to get fired."

   YOU COULD SAY:
   A. I'm sure she'll tell us herself if it happens.
   B. She's always goofing off. That's why.
   C. Really? When is her last day?
   D. Wait till I tell her brother!

4. "Last night the boss really yelled at Eddy for not sweeping the storeroom."

   YOU COULD SAY:
   A. What did the boss say to him?
   B. So old Eddy really got it, huh!
   C. Wow, I wish I could have been there.
   D. I guess I'd better not forget to sweep the storeroom tonight.

HOW AM I DOING IN GETTING ALONG WITH OTHERS?

The Rockin' Rollers band sounds great! That's because they get along with each other on the job.

THEY:
HELP EACH OTHER
STAND UP FOR EACH OTHER
ARE FRIENDLY TO EACH OTHER
KNOW HOW TO TAKE CRITICISM

THEY DON'T:
BOSS EACH OTHER AROUND
FIGHT
COMPLAIN
GOSSIP

SELF QUIZ

Circle the answers that tell how you act at work.

HOW I ACT...	#1	#2	#3
1. I gossip about my co-workers.	USUALLY	SOMETIMES	HARDLY EVER
2. I am agreeable.	HARDLY EVER	SOMETIMES	USUALLY
3. I am bossy.	USUALLY	SOMETIMES	HARDLY EVER
4. I am friendly to co-workers.	HARDLY EVER	SOMETIMES	USUALLY
5. If someone puts me down, I laugh it off.	HARDLY EVER	SOMETIMES	USUALLY
6. I can take criticism without blaming others.	HARDLY EVER	SOMETIMES	USUALLY
7. I try to stop gossip at work.	HARDLY EVER	SOMETIMES	USUALLY
8. When I am criticized I feel picked-on.	USUALLY	SOMETIMES	HARDLY EVER
9. I try to help my co-workers.	HARDLY EVER	SOMETIMES	USUALLY
10. I ignore put-downs.	HARDLY EVER	SOMETIMES	USUALLY
11. I pout at work.	USUALLY	SOMETIMES	HARDLY EVER
12. I ask for things in a friendly way.	HARDLY EVER	SOMETIMES	USUALLY

TO SCORE YOURSELF, TURN PAGE UPSIDE DOWN.

SCORING YOURSELF: Did you check any answers in column #1? If you did, you need to improve in those areas.

HOW CAN I IMPROVE IN GETTING ALONG WITH OTHERS?

The cards below tell you what you *should* do at work to get along with others. Copy the card that shows where you need to improve most. (Read your answers on page 54 and page 59 if you are not sure where to improve.)

Carry your copy of the card with you. Put a mark in the box each time you do what it says. Each mark is 1 point. Decide ahead of time how many points you want to get. If you don't have a job, use the card at school. Other students will be "co-workers."

_____   _____   _____
Where I want to improve   How many points I want to get   Date(s) I will keep track

ACCEPT CRITICISM WELL	BE FRIENDLY TO CO-WORKERS	DON'T BE BOSSY
STAND UP FOR A CO-WORKER WHO IS BEING GOSSIPED ABOUT	HELP CO-WORKERS	_____ Your own idea

By now you have an idea of where you should improve in getting along with others at work. A GAME Plan can help you improve. Read the GAME Plan below to see one way to improve in Accepting Criticism.

WHO?	DOES WHAT?	HOW?	WHY?	HOW DO WE KNOW?
Davida, her supervisor	Davida takes criticism from her supervisor without blaming others for a week Start: Monday Finish: Friday	When criticized, Davida will say, "I'm sorry, I'll get it right next time."	**+** Supervisor will pay for Davida's lunch on Friday **—** Davida will pay for supervisor's lunch on Friday	Davida's supervisor will decide which one owes for lunch on Friday

Fill out the GAME Plan for yourself. Check the Self-Quiz on page 59 to help you decide where you need improvement.

WHO?	DOES WHAT?	HOW?	WHY?	HOW DO WE KNOW?

61

6. FOLLOWING DIRECTIONS On the Job

WHAT'S FOLLOWING DIRECTIONS ALL ABOUT?

Grocery baggers at the Mini-Mart have to do other tasks too. Here is what they are supposed to do:

BAG GROCERIES
SWEEP
CARRY GROCERIES OUT
LOAD GROCERIES INTO CARS
BRING CARTS IN FROM PARKING LOT

Read what these five baggers at Mini-Mart do at work. You be the judge — who gets 1st prize for doing what she or he is *supposed to do*? Put a 1 in that person's ribbon. Then decide who gets 2nd, 3rd, 4th, and 5th prizes.

Sue bags and carries out groceries. She does not like to help people load, so she collects carts instead

Donna bags and carries out groceries. She collects carts after she helps people load. She sweeps the front when she's not busy.

Laszlo likes to talk to the customers when he carries their groceries out to their cars. He walks around the parking lot to get out of doing work inside. His boss often has to call Laszlo to come back in the store.

Cassie carries out groceries. She likes to go out to collect carts. She never sweeps.

Hafer bags and carries out groceries. He doesn't like to help load cars. He stands by the cars waiting for the customers to take the bags.

DOING
WHAT
YOU ARE
SUPPOSED
TO DO

Who got 1st prize and WHY? _____

Who got last prize and WHY? _____

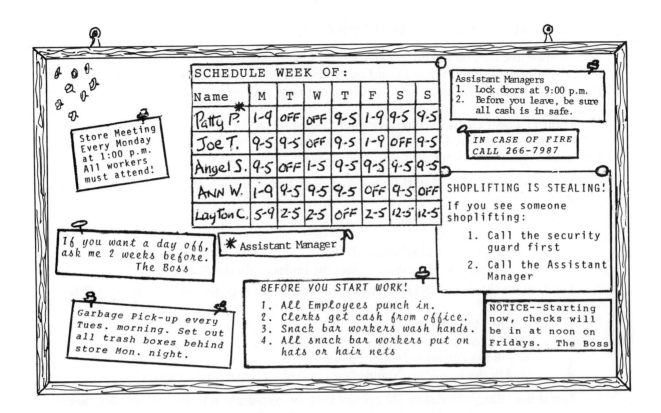

Store Meeting Every Monday at 1:00 p.m. All workers must attend!

SCHEDULE WEEK OF:

Name	M	T	W	T	F	S	S
Patty P.*	1-9	OFF	OFF	9-5	1-9	9-5	9-5
Joe T.	9-5	9-5	OFF	9-5	1-9	OFF	9-5
Angel S.	9-5	OFF	1-5	9-5	9-5	9-5	9-5
Ann W.	1-9	9-5	9-5	9-5	OFF	9-5	OFF
Layton C.	5-9	2-5	2-5	OFF	2-5	12-5	12-5

* Assistant Manager

Assistant Managers
1. Lock doors at 9:00 p.m.
2. Before you leave, be sure all cash is in safe.

IN CASE OF FIRE CALL 266-7987

SHOPLIFTING IS STEALING!
If you see someone shoplifting:
1. Call the security guard first
2. Call the Assistant Manager

If you want a day off, ask me 2 weeks before. The Boss

BEFORE YOU START WORK!
1. All Employees punch in.
2. Clerks get cash from office.
3. Snack bar workers wash hands.
4. All snack bar workers put on hats or hair nets

Garbage Pick-up every Tues. morning. Set out all trash boxes behind store Mon. night.

NOTICE--Starting now, checks will be in at noon on Fridays.   The Boss

This is the bulletin board at Lindy's Department Store. It tells workers *when* things should be done. Read the notes on the board and answer the questions below.

1. What is the date and time of the next store meeting? _____

2. Patty came in to work at 2:00 on Monday. Was that the right time? _____

3. What time should Joe punch out on Tuesday? _____

4. Who is the Assistant Manager for the week? _____

5. At 9:10 P.M. Monday night, the store was full of shoppers. When should the Assistant Manager have locked the door? _____

6. What must Assistant Managers do before they leave? _____

7. When should the garbage be taken out? _____

8. If Ann's dad comes in Friday at 10 A.M. to pick up her check for her, how long will he have to wait for it? _____

9. What is the one thing that all employees should do before starting work? _____

10. If Layton wants October 25th off, when should he ask for it off? _____

11. If an employee sees someone shoplifting, who should he or she call first? _____

12. When would you call 266-7987? _____

DOING THINGS *WHEN* YOU ARE SUPPOSED TO

You follow directions on the job when you do things in the RIGHT ORDER. *If you are not sure what the right order is, you should ask your boss or supervisor.* Read the stories below. Decide what Len and Elaine should do. Circle the right answers.

Len works in a restaurant. His boss gives him these directions: "Come in at 11:00. If the dirty tables are not cleared, clear the tables. Then do the dirty dishes. If it starts to get busy, wait on the customers by filling their water glasses."

1. Len comes in at 11:00 and there are four dirty tables. What is the first thing he should do?
    a. Clear the dirty tables
    b. Do the dishes
    c. Fill the customers' water glasses
    d. Ask his boss if he should clear the tables or do the dishes

2. Len is doing the dishes and notices that the restaurant is getting busy. What should he do now?
    a. Clear the dirty tables
    b. Keep on doing the dishes
    c. Fill the customers' water glasses
    d. Ask the boss if he should clear the tables or wait on customers

3. Len is busy doing the dishes. He notices that the restaurant is really getting busy. Some customers are waiting for their water, but there are also many dirty tables. He should:
    a. Clear the dirty tables
    b. Keep on doing the dishes
    c. Fill the customers' water glasses
    d. Ask his boss if he should wait on customers or clear the tables

Elaine bags groceries in a supermarket. Her boss tells her, "Put the heavy items on the bottom of the bag. Put the soft items on the top." The boss also says to wrap frozen foods in a separate plastic bag.

1. The checker hands Elaine some bread to pack. Elaine should:
    a. Put it on the bottom of the bag
    b. Put it on the top of the bag
    c. Wrap it in a separate plastic bag
    d. Ask the checker what to do

2. The checker gives Elaine some cans to pack. Elaine should:
    a. Put them on the bottom of the bag
    b. Put them on the top of the bag
    c. Wrap them in a separate plastic bag
    d. Ask the checker what to do

3. Elaine knows that the soft or breakable items go on the top of the bag. She does not know if she should put the bread on the top or the eggs on the top. She should:
    a. Put the bread and eggs on the bottom of the bag
    b. Put the bread in the bag last, on top of the eggs
    c. Put the eggs in the bag last, on top of the bread
    d. Ask the checker which one goes in the bag first

DOING THINGS *WHERE* YOU ARE SUPPOSED TO

You can follow directions better if you have the whole picture of where you work. You can see how your job fits in with all the rest. This will help you remember what to do where.

Below is Neal Baxter's picture of where he works. It shows the PEOPLE and PLACES he works with, and what he does in each place.

RAINBOW CHILD CARE CENTER

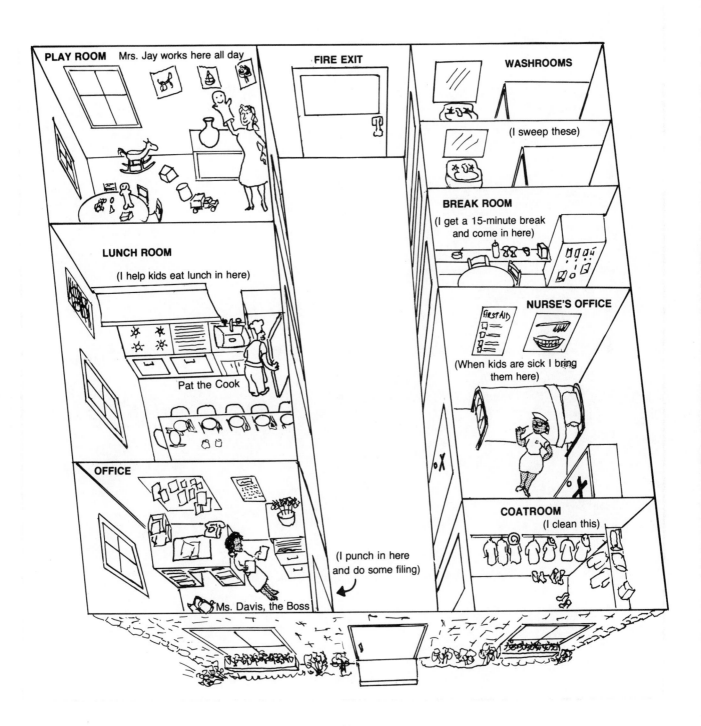

WHAT'S FOLLOWING DIRECTIONS ALL ABOUT?

Draw the place where you work. Put in the PEOPLE and PLACES you work with. Write in WHAT you do in each PLACE. If you don't have a job, draw your home and write in where you do tasks there. Or draw your school and what you do there during the week. You can draw a simple floor plan with stick figures.

_____

Where You Work

NOT QUITE RIGHT WORKERS

Read about the workers below. Did they follow directions about
   — WHAT work was done
   or WHEN work was done
   or doing work in the RIGHT ORDER
   or WHERE work was done?

1. Lou's boss told him to go to the restroom to put on his hat. Lou put his hat on by the grill where he was working.

    DID LOU FOLLOW DIRECTIONS? _____

    IF NOT, WHAT DID HE DO WRONG? _____

2. Marlyn works in a dress shop. Her boss told her to thank customers and tell them she hopes they will come in again. When Marlyn rang up a sale, she handed the package to the customer and said "thanks."

    DID MARLYN FOLLOW DIRECTIONS? _____

    IF NOT, WHAT DID SHE DO WRONG? _____

3. Jeff stocks shelves. His boss told him to take the garbage out before starting work Monday morning. Jeff took the garbage out before he left work Sunday night.

    DID JEFF FOLLOW DIRECTIONS? _____

    IF NOT, WHAT DID HE DO WRONG? _____

4. Roy's boss told him, "Count the money in the cash register before you start work." Roy started work at 4 P.M. He counted the money at 5 P.M.

    DID ROY FOLLOW DIRECTIONS? _____

    IF NOT, WHAT DID HE DO WRONG? _____

5. Leah delivers packages. When she is done with work, she is supposed to: park the truck, turn in the money and keys, punch out. Leah parked the truck, turned in the money and punched out.

    DID LEAH FOLLOW DIRECTIONS? _____

    IF NOT, WHAT DID SHE DO WRONG? _____

HOW AM I DOING AT FOLLOWING DIRECTIONS?

WHAT DO I DO?

To be good at following directions, you have to know what your tasks at work are. Here is a list of job tasks made by an employee at a clothing store.

> ### The Jeans Shop
>
> List of Job Tasks
>
> 1. Punch time card
> 2. Get change for cash register from office
> 3. Put price tags on new jeans
> 4. Stack jeans neatly
> 5. Wait on customers
> 6. Punch out
>
> Do When Not Busy
>
> Shine glass doors
> Sweep dressing room floors

Make your own list of WHAT you do at work. Describe your job tasks in the order that you do them. If you don't have a job, list the tasks you have at home and at school each day.

Where You Work

List of Tasks

1. _____
2. _____
3. _____
4. _____
5. _____
6. _____

Do When Not Busy

_____

_____

_____

This chart will help you figure out how well you follow directions at work, home, or school. The headings at the top of the chart tell what you should do to follow directions. Rate yourself by circling the number that shows how you work. Then you can see at a glance how you're doing. If you can, have your boss rate you, too.

	DOING *WHAT* IS SUPPOSED TO BE DONE	DOING THINGS *WHEN* THEY SHOULD BE DONE	DOING THINGS IN THE *RIGHT ORDER*	DOING THINGS *WHERE* THEY SHOULD BE DONE
Excellent	5	5	5	5
Good	4	4	4	4
Satisfactory	3	3	3	3
Needs Improvement	2	2	2	2
Danger of Being Fired	1	1	1	1

DOING THINGS IN THE *RIGHT ORDER*

69

HOW CAN I IMPROVE IN FOLLOWING DIRECTIONS?

THE FABULOUS FOLLOWING DIRECTIONS FIXER

To improve in following directions, describe your job tasks on the lines below. (Go back to page 62 if you need to.) Check (√) every day if you have done them the right way. If you *did not* follow directions, give yourself a zero (○). Every day ask your employer to look at your chart after work. If your employer thinks you did not follow directions, she or he should put a ○ around your √. Try to get all √'s.

JOB TASKS	M	T	W	T	F	S	S
1. _____							
2. _____							
3. _____							
4. _____							
5. _____							
6. _____							
EMPLOYER'S INITIALS							

Jerry works at the Jeans Shop. Here is Jerry's Fabulous Following Directions Fixer.

JOB TASKS *Jerry Freitas*	M	T	W	T	F	S	S
1. Punch time card	√	√	√				
2. Get change from office	√	√	√				
3. Put price tags on new jeans	○	√	√				
4. Stack jeans neatly	√	Ø	√				
5. Wait on customers	√	√	√				
6. Punch out	√	√	√				
EMPLOYER'S INTITIALS	RK	RK	RK				

On Monday, Jerry forgot to put the price tags on the new jeans. He gave himself a ○. On Tuesday, he thought he had stacked the jeans neatly. His employer did not think so, so he circled the √. On Wednesday, Jerry did everything the right way.

70

By now you have an idea of where you should improve in following directions. The GAME Plan below shows how Juan improved in WHAT he is supposed to do.

WHO?	DOES WHAT?	HOW?	WHY?	HOW DO WE KNOW?
Juan, his employer	Juan will finish all his job tasks Start: Monday Finish: Friday	Juan fills out a Fabulous Following Directions Fixer (F.F.D.F.)	**+** Juan will get a raise **–** Juan will not get a raise	At the end of the week, Juan and his employer will look at the F.F.D.F. to see how Juan did

Make a GAME Plan of your own. In the DOES WHAT? column will go what you want to improve in. Remember that the keys to following directions are: Doing WHAT you are supposed to; Doing things WHEN you should; Doing things in the RIGHT ORDER; Doing things WHERE they should be done.

WHO?	DOES WHAT?	HOW?	WHY?	HOW DO WE KNOW?

7. TREATING CUSTOMERS WELL
On the Job

WHAT'S TREATING CUSTOMERS WELL ALL ABOUT?

THE FRIENDLY GREETING

The way you greet customers is very important. If they don't feel welcome, they won't come back again. If the company you work for doesn't do well, your job won't go very well either. The more you can do for your company's business, the better your job will be.

A friendly greeting has three parts.

1. You start it with a *smile*.

2. Then give a friendly greeting like *"Hello"* or *"Good morning."*

3. Try to add a few words that will make the customer feel welcome and special. For example, you might smile and say: *"Good morning. How are you today?"*

A greeting that is not friendly makes people feel that you don't care if they come back or not. An example of a greeting that is not friendly might be:

"Okay. It's your turn. What do you want?"

A customer who hears this will not feel welcome.

WHAT'S TREATING CUSTOMERS WELL ALL ABOUT?

Here are some things that workers say to customers. Put a plus sign (+) in front of the friendly greetings. Put a minus sign (−) in front of the greetings that are not friendly. The first two are done for you.

1. __+__ "Good morning. I see you're up early."

2. __−__ "You're next. Come on. Make it snappy."

3. _____ "What are you looking for?"

4. _____ "Hi! Isn't it a nice day?"

5. _____ "It's good to see you, Mrs. Santucci. Is your daughter still working at Raul's hardware?"

6. _____ "Okay. Let's go."

7. _____ "Welcome to Argus. May I help you?"

8. _____ "I can't help you. I'm busy."

9. _____ "Hello. How are you today?"

10. _____ "Hello Wendy. How's school coming along?"

11. _____ "Good afternoon. Is this your first time at Hunter's?"

12. _____ "I don't want to rush you but we close in fifteen minutes."

13. _____ "Whew. It's hot in here."

14. _____ "I'm busy right now. Could you come back later?"

If your boss wants you to greet people in a certain way, write it here:

_____

BEING POLITE TO CUSTOMERS

HEY, PAL! YOU FORGOT YOUR CHANGE!

What do you think the employee is saying wrong in the picture?

_____

_____

Being polite to a customer is very important. There are at least four ways of being polite to customers:

- Use a customer's NAME, if you know it.
- Call a woman MISS or MA'AM; call a man SIR.
- Say EXCUSE ME to get the attention of a customer.
- FIND OUT what the customer wants to know. If you don't know the answer to a customer's question, *don't* say: "I don't know." Tell the customer, "I'm sorry, I don't know, but I will find out for you."

Below are listed polite and impolite ways to talke to customers. Draw a line through the impolite ways.

"Hey, kid, c'mere!"

"Yes, ma'am, do you see anything you like?"

"Don't ask me. I don't know where your order is."

"What's your problem, buddy?"

"Sir, if you need help, just let me know."

"Pardon me, would you care for any help?"

"Yeah, lady, what are you looking for?"

"Excuse me, can I help you?"

"I'm sorry. I don't know, but I will find out."

WHAT SHOULD I SAY?

Read the stories below. Before you answer the question, think about the four ways of being polite to customers.

1. You are working at a cash register. A man starts to walk away without his change. What might you say to him?

_____

2. A woman brings her little girl into the store where you work. While the woman is shopping, the girl starts to go out the door alone. You have to stay behind the counter. What might you say to the woman?

_____

3. You're a clerk in a furniture store. A sale is on. Mr. and Mrs. Johnson ask you how long the sale will last. You don't know. What might you say?

_____

4. Mr. Carver is carrying a shopping bag. The bag has a hole in it. A small box falls out of the bag. Mr. Carver doesn't know it has fallen out. What might you do and say?

_____

5. You are a waiter in a restaurant. You have just taken a woman's order. You forgot to ask her how she wants her steak done. When you go back to the table, what might you say to her?

_____

6. You work in a bakery. Mr. Flora comes in to pick up a cake. While you wrap it up, he starts to read the paper. The cake is ready. Mr. Flora is reading. What might you say to Mr. Flora?

_____

7. Mr. Feldman calls up the Davidson Sport Shop where you work. He asks if the store is still out of motorcycle helmets. You look. You find out the store still does not have any helmets. What might you say to Mr. Feldman?

_____

8. You're a stock clerk at Diamond Grocery Store. A woman asks you where the cheese is. You know it's in Aisle 4 at the other end of the store. What might you say and do?

_____

9. You work at a gas station. A student from your school drives up. She sits in the car reading while you fill up the gas tank. You have to ask her if she wants the oil checked. You don't know her name and the windows are rolled up. What might you do and say?

_____

WHAT'S TREATING CUSTOMERS WELL ALL ABOUT?

10. You're working in a clothing store. An older couple comes up to you. They ask for directions to a new restaurant in town. You've never heard of the restaurant. What might you do and say to this couple?

   _____

11. Brenda, a student from your school, comes to the restaurant where you work. Brenda's bill is $5.00. She gives you a $2.00 bill, and starts to walk away. What might you say to Brenda?

   _____

12. You're a clerk at Blue Square Hardware Store. Tim, a customer, asks you the price of a wrench. You don't know the price. But you do know where you can find it in the price book. What might you do and say?

   _____

EXTRA HELP FOR CUSTOMERS

Some customers who may need extra help are:

      elderly people
      parents with babies
      handicapped people
      people who don't speak English as their native language

Most of the time, such customers want to do things for themselves. The best help you can give is to respect the customer's independence. If you think a customer needs extra help, *ask first*: "May I help you?"

HELPING AN OLDER CUSTOMER

Some older people may not see or hear as well as you do. Some are not very strong. Not all older people have these problems. You will have to pay attention to older customers to see if they need your help.

Here are some things you may be able to do to help older people. Fill in the missing word.

Offer to _____ things down
if they are hard to remember.

Open a _____ .

Offer to _____ signs and menus.

Talk _____ and clear
so the person hears you.

Offer to _____ a heavy bag
or package.

76

HELPING CUSTOMERS WITH BABIES

Fathers or mothers with small babies may need extra help. They have their hands full! These are things you can sometimes do to help customers with small babies:

Open a door
Carry a package
Get something that's out of reach

_____

(your own idea)

HELPING CUSTOMERS ON CRUTCHES

A customer on crutches may need help getting through a door or finding a place to sit in a crowded restaurant. A customer who puts crutches aside to sit down will still want to have the crutches close by. Never take a customer's crutches away unless the person asks you to.

Think of two ways you may be able to help a customer on crutches:

1. _____

2. _____

HELPING CUSTOMERS WHO DON'T SPEAK ENGLISH AS THEIR NATIVE LANGUAGE

Give extra time to customers who don't know much English. Be patient and do your best to figure out what the customer is saying. Most people can *understand* more of a foreign language than they can *speak*. So speak clearly yourself, and smile. Point to what you are talking about if that will help.

Two more ways you may be able to help the non-English-speaking customer:

1. _____

2. _____

HELPING A BLIND CUSTOMER

A blind customer will need some extra help, but will not want to be treated like someone who is helpless. Don't just take over. Always *ask* first if you can help. The blind customer will *tell* you how you can help.

Some common-sense things you can do for blind customers:

Put change in the person's hand
Say out loud how much the bill is
Tell the person what you are doing

Other things you can do:

1. _____

2. _____

HELPING A CUSTOMER IN A WHEELCHAIR

People in wheelchairs sometimes cannot reach things. *Offer* to help a wheelchair customer before actually doing anything. This shows you respect that person's independence.

Ask these people how they might help a wheelchair customer, and write their answers below:

Your boss _____

_____

Another worker _____

_____

Yourself _____

_____

HELPING THE CUSTOMER WITH POOR HEARING

It's not always obvious that a customer has poor hearing. You might see that a customer is wearing a hearing aid. Maybe you'll see two or more customers talking to each other with rapid hand movements, or sign language. But not everyone who has a hearing problem wears a hearing aid or uses sign language.

If a customer seems to have trouble hearing you, the best thing you can do is look at the person when you talk.

Some hearing-impaired people can read lips. Even people who can't read lips will understand better and feel better if they can see your face and mouth.

If a customer turns his or her ear toward you, just make your voice *deeper*. Don't yell or talk extra slow — it will confuse the hearer. A smile always helps.

THE ANGRY CUSTOMER

Every person on the job runs into an angry customer once in a while. Here are some guidelines to follow when a customer gets mad.

1. *LISTEN* TO WHAT THE CUSTOMER IS SAYING.

2. SAY YOU ARE SORRY.
   Even if the problem was not your fault, you should say you are sorry that it happened.

3. EXPLAIN WHY THE PROBLEM MIGHT HAVE HAPPENED.
   When the customer knows the reason for the problem, she or he might cool off.

4. TRY TO SOLVE THE PROBLEM.
   If you're not sure you can solve the problem, go to your employer and ask for help.

5. CONTACT YOUR BOSS RIGHT AWAY, if the customer is very angry.

6. ABOVE ALL, STAY COOL YOURSELF.

WHAT'S TREATING CUSTOMERS WELL ALL ABOUT?

WHAT WOULD YOU DO?

Here are some stories about angry customers. You are the worker. Finish each story by writing down what you would say or do.

1. CARDOZO CLEANERS

    Mr. Brewner calls Cardozo's and is told his dry cleaning is done. When he comes by to get his clothes, they aren't ready. The trip was for nothing. He's mad.

    You didn't tell Mr. Brewner that his clothes were done. Someone from the morning shift must have told him that. You know the clothes won't be ready until tomorrow.

    "I would like to know why my clothes aren't ready," he demands. "I was told they were done."

    You say and do: _____

    _____

2. HAMBURGER STOP

    Today is very busy at the Hamburger Stop. Two other workers are out sick. The orders are way behind. You are working as fast as you can.

    One of the regular customers, Mrs. McMann, has been waiting ten minutes. Her lunch break is only half an hour long. She's hungry and impatient. She taps the counter with her fingers and stares at you.

    You say and do: _____

    _____

3. JEEVES' JEANS

    A girl has come into the store with some jeans she bought last week. The first time she washed them, they fell apart. She's showing you the jeans, and she's upset.

    You know that the store won't take back any clothes that have been worn or washed.

    The girl hands you the jeans and says, "I want my money back."

    You say and do: _____

    _____

4. BREEN'S SHOES

    A customer ordered a pair of shoes from Breen's almost a month ago. The first time she came in to get them, they were the wrong color. Now they're the wrong size. She is standing at your counter and she is very angry.

    You say and do: _____

    _____

YOUR OWN STORY

Write what happened when you had an angry customer. What did the customer say and do? What did you say and do? If you have never had to deal with an angry customer, write about one you've seen. Then explain what you would do if you had that customer.

"How I Took Care of an Angry Customer"

WHAT'S TREATING CUSTOMERS WELL ALL ABOUT?

WHEN THE CUSTOMER LEAVES

When a customer leaves, you should always:

> *Smile*
> *Say "Thank You"*
> *Add some friendly words*

Customers should always feel you were glad they came. This is true even if they didn't buy anything. If you say something pleasant, they will want to come back again. Here are some ways of saying *"Thanks for coming:"*

"Thank you. Come back again soon."

"Thank you for shopping at Johnson's."

"Was everything all right, ma'am?"

"Did you find what you were looking for, Mr. Okuru?"

"Thank you. Have a good day."

"Can I help you carry these to your car?"

"May I hold the door for you?"

"I hope you'll come back for our sale next week."

"It was nice to see you again."

Can you think of other ways to say goodbye to customers? Write three of them below. If your boss has taught you a certain way, make sure you put it on your list.

1. _____

2. _____

3. _____

HOW AM I DOING IN TREATING CUSTOMERS WELL?

For each sentence below, check the answer that tells how *you* are doing in treating customers well. If you check "other", write in what you do.

1. When customers come in, I

_____ Smile and give a friendly greeting

_____ Say nothing

_____ Look the other way

_____ Other _____

2. When talking to customers, I

_____ Usually just say, "Hey"

_____ Say, "Sir", "Ma'am", or "Excuse me"

_____ Just start talking

_____ Other _____

3. When customers ask about something and I don't know the answer, I

_____ Tell them to ask someone else

_____ Say, "I'm sorry. I don't know."

_____ Say, I don't know, but I will find out for you."

_____ Other _____

4. When customers are leaving, I

_____ Say goodbye and some nice words

_____ Say nothing

_____ Say goodbye

_____ Other _____

5. If a handicapped person comes in, I

_____ Look the other way

_____ Start helping the person

_____ Ask the person, "May I help you?"

_____ Other _____

6. When a customer complains, I

_____ Listen and try to solve the problem

_____ Complain back

_____ Don't do anything

_____ Other _____

7. If a customer gets very mad, I

_____ Get mad and yell back

_____ Call the manager

_____ Don't know what to do

_____ Other _____

8. When older customers come in, I

_____ Look the other way

_____ Start talking real loud

_____ Watch to see if they need extra help

_____ Other _____

9. When regular customers come in, I

_____ Say the same thing I say to other customers

_____ Say nothing

_____ Call them by name

_____ Other _____

10. If a customer doesn't speak English well, I

_____ Listen and watch carefully to see if I can understand him or her

_____ Yell loud so the person can hear me

_____ Call someone else to wait on this person.

_____ Other _____

Discuss your answer in class. Find out how other students think you are doing in treating customers well.

84

This chart will help you find out how well you treat customers on the job. Check (√) the column that best describes the way you act with customers. Ask your boss to read your answers and check the ones she or he agrees with.

In waiting on customer, do I:	USUALLY	SOMETIMES	HARDLY EVER	EMPLOYER AGREES
Smile?				
Give a friendly greeting?				
Say goodbye in a friendly way?				
Call customers by their names?				
Use polite words such as "Sir", "Ma'am, or "Excuse me?"				
Listen and be polite when a customer gets angry?				
Help customers with babies?				
Help older customers?				
Help handicapped customers?				
Help customers who don't speak English well?				
Help customers who ask for my help?				

HOW CAN I IMPROVE IN TREATING CUSTOMERS WELL?

Do you know what everyone's favorite word is? It's his or her own name. Customers like it when you call them by name. It makes them feel good. It makes them feel welcome.

Ask your employer or other workers what the names of your regular customers are. Learn the names so that when you see one of these customers, you can say, "Hi, Mrs. Sanchez" or "Hello, Pete."

Write down the names of customers who come in once a week or more:

_____

_____

_____

_____

Keep a list of these names at work. The list will help you remember the name that goes with a familiar face.

By now you have an idea of where you should improve in treating customers well. Read the GAME Plan below to see how Ilona improved in saying goodbye to customers.

WHO?	DOES WHAT?	HOW?	WHY?	HOW DO WE KNOW?
Ilona, her boss	When customers pay, Ilona will: Smile Say thank you Add some friendly words Ilona will do this to 5 customers every day. Start: Monday Finish: Friday	On a card next to the cash register, Ilona checks (√) each time she does these things for a customer Boss will notice when she does not do these things	**+** Ilona has been promised a permanent job if she can improve in handling customers **−** Ilona will not get the permanent job	Ilona looks at the card at the end of each day, and reviews her progress with her boss

Make your own GAME Plan to help you treat customers well. The chart you did on page 85 will show you where you need to improve.

WHO?	DOES WHAT?	HOW?	WHY?	HOW DO WE KNOW?

8. JOB-RELATED SKILLS

WHERE DO I LOOK FOR A JOB?

Knowing where to look for a job can be hard. Some of the people, places and organizations that can help you are listed on this page. Find them in the cloud below. When you find them, put them in the right spaces at the bottom of the page. The first letters are already filled in for you.

Telephone Book

School Work Program

Friends

State Employment Office

School Counselor

Relatives

Teachers

C.E.T.A.

School Placement Office

Want Ads

F_____

S_____ C_____

S_____ E_____ O_____

S_____ W_____ P_____

S_____ P_____

R_____

W_____ A_____

T_____ B_____

C_____

T_____

O_____

USE PERSONAL CONTACTS TO FIND A JOB

Sometimes you can find a job by talking to someone you know. That someone could be a neighbor, friend, relative, or an adult at school. Fill in the blanks below to learn about using personal contacts to find a job. Use the words in the box.

STORES   WORK   DAY   YOU   TEACHERS

NEIGHBORHOOD   LOOKING   UNCLE   UP

1. Your parents might know a friend at _____ who knows of a possible job for you.
     _ _ □ _

2. What about contacting your aunt or _____ ?
     □ _ _ _ _

3. Ask your guidance counselors and _____ if they can help you.
     _ _ □ _ _ _ _ _

4. Local _____ or other businesses may have job openings.
     _ _ □ _ _ _

5. You have to keep at it every _____ .
     □ _ _

6. Ask the people in your _____ for help.
     □ _ _ _ _ _ _ _ _ _ _ _

7. Keep _____ !
     _ _ □ _ _ _ _

8. Don't give _____ !
     □ _

9. The one who gets a job from all this work is _____ .
     □ _ _

Now take the letters from the boxes and place them here:

    _ _ _ _ _ _ _ _ _

Unscramble the letters and discover a good way to find jobs. Two letters are already filled in for you.

LOOK RIGHT   A _ _ _ _ _   Y _ _ !!!

89

JOB-RELATED SKILLS

HUNTING JOBS?

Below are want ads like the ones you can find in your local newspaper. Match the worker with the job. Put the letter of the ad on the line in front of the worker who is listed in the ad.

A | **Driver's Asst. Foreman**
Experienced in directing, scheduling and supervising other drivers. For catering company whose drivers deliver food in vans. Central location. Mon-Fri 6:30am-6pm. 384-3100.

B | **BANK TELLERS**
$650-$850 Mo. Co. Pays Fee Comm'l, Univ., Savings, Supv. A-E-S 11 E. Adams 922-0185

C | KEYPUNCH OPERATORS
Experienced keypunch operators. Full time. 1st & 2nd shifts. Experience on 3742 helpful.
Beacon Data Processing
3603 W. Cortland
235-9625
Equal Opportunity Employer

D | **Exp. Waitresses Wanted**
Must be over 21. Inquire at ENC Snack Shop & Liquors, Armitage & Western.

E | **BEAUTICIANS**
Busy unisex shop. Earn $300+ a week. Paid vac. Bolinbrook. Call Ralph 759-9808.

F | **Auto Tow Truck Drivers**
Exp,d, top pay 1301 Fullerton

1. _____ Babysitter

2. _____ Cakemaker

3. _____ Hardware Clerk

4. _____ Snack Shop Waitress

5. _____ Experienced Tow Truck Driver

6. _____ Furnace Operator

7. _____ Cook

8. _____ Beautician

9. _____ Dental Technician

10. _____ Driver Supervisor

11. _____ Bank Teller

12. _____ Experienced Keypunch Operator

G | **Hardware Clerk**
Must have at least 3 years retail hardware experience. No Evenings   No Sundays Permanent   Good Pay
ACE HARDWARE
949 N. State St.   787-9547

H | GRILL COOKS
Good Pay, Benefits, Permanent. Days, Free Meals. 55 E. Monroe Rm. 35 No Calls

I | **BAKER,** Cake Maker & Decorator. Experienced. Position open for full time work. Top salary paid. Please call: 266-2020 8am-6pm or Apply in person at The French Pastry Shop, 1640 N. Wells St.

J | **Dental Technician** 2 positions available. Crown & bridge technicians, make gold crowns & bridges. 2 yrs education & dental tech school req'd. $250 per wk. Contact Steven Brandhandler, Coty Dental Lab. 679-7670.

K | **Heat Treat Asst Foreman**
N. side comm'l steel treating company seeking an experienced furnace operator. 3rd shift. Excellent salary & benefits. Call Mr. Fitzgerald. 338-5700

L | BABYSITTER for 2 children. Lady to live in, over 40, rm & bd + salary. 339-5202.

WHAT'S UP IN THE WANT ADS?

Look through the newspapers. Find four Help Wanted ads that interest you. Cut them out and paste them below. Then answer the questions.

	PASTE WANT AD HERE	PASTE WANT AD HERE	PASTE WANT AD HERE	PASTE WANT AD HERE
Could you do this job?				
Why would you like to do this job?				
Whom or where do you call for the job?				
Do you need experience for the job?				
What is one thing you like and one thing you don't like about the job?	Like: Don't Like:	Like: Don't Like:	Like: Don't Like:	Like: Don't Like:

JOB-RELATED SKILLS

SOCIAL SECURITY

What is Social Security?

When you get a job, money is taken out of your paycheck for the Social Security Tax. When you retire, or if you get hurt badly, you and your family will get money from Social Security.

How do I get a Social Security number?

Go to your Social Security Office and fill out a card. In six weeks or so, you will get your Social Security card. You'll need it to get a job.

Here is a Social Security application form. Practice filling it out.

FORM SS-5 — APPLICATION FOR A SOCIAL SECURITY NUMBER CARD (Original, Replacement or Correction)

INSTRUCTIONS   Type or print, using pen with dark blue or black ink. Do not use pencil.

NAA	NAME TO BE SHOWN ON CARD	First	Middle	Last
NAB **1**	FULL NAME AT BIRTH (IF OTHER THAN ABOVE)	First	Middle	Last
ONA	OTHER NAME(S) USED			

STT 2 MAILING ADDRESS   (Street/Apt. No., P.O. Box, Rural Route No.)

CTY CITY (Do not abbreviate)   **STE** STATE   **ZIP** ZIP CODE

CSP 3 CITIZENSHIP (Check one only)
- ☐ a. U.S. citizen
- ☐ b. Legal alien allowed to work
- ☐ c. Legal alien not allowed to work
- ☐ d. Other (See instructions on Page 2)

SEX 4 SEX
- ☐ MALE
- ☐ FEMALE

ETB 5 RACE/ETHNIC DESCRIPTION (Check one only) (Voluntary)
- ☐ a. Asian, Asian-American or Pacific Islander (Includes persons of Chinese, Filipino, Japanese, Korean, Samoan, etc., ancestry or descent)
- ☐ b. Hispanic (Includes persons of Chicano, Cuban, Mexican or Mexican-American, Puerto Rican, South or Central American, or other Spanish ancestry or descent)
- ☐ c. Negro or Black (not Hispanic)
- ☐ d. Northern American Indian or Alaskan Native
- ☐ e. White (not Hispanic)

DOB 6	AGE 7	PLB 8		FCI
DATE OF BIRTH ► MONTH / DAY / YEAR	PRESENT AGE	PLACE OF BIRTH ► CITY (Do not abbreviate)	STATE OR FOREIGN COUNTRY (Do not abbreviate)	☐

MNA **9**	MOTHER'S NAME AT HER BIRTH	First	Middle	Last (Her maiden name)
FNA	FATHER'S NAME	First	Middle	Last

PNO 10
a. Has a Social Security number card ever been requested for the person listed in item 1?   ☐ YES(2)   ☐ NO(1)   ☐ Don't know(1)

b. Was a card received for the person listed in item 1?   ☐ YES(3)   ☐ NO(1)   ☐ Don't know(1)

▶ **IF YOU CHECKED YES TO A OR B, COMPLETE ITEMS C THROUGH E; OTHERWISE GO TO ITEM 11.**

SSN c. Enter the Social Security number assigned to the person listed in item 1.   ☐☐☐ — ☐☐ — ☐☐☐☐

NLC d. Enter the name shown on the most recent Social Security card issued for the person listed in item 1.

PDB   e. Date of birth correction (See Instruction 10 on page 2) ► MONTH / DAY / YEAR

DON 11 TODAY'S DATE ► MONTH / DAY / YEAR

12 Telephone number where we can reach you during the day. Please include the area code. ► HOME / OTHER

13 YOUR SIGNATURE

14 YOUR RELATIONSHIP TO PERSON IN ITEM 1   ☐ Self   ☐ Other (Specify)

REFERENCES

What is a reference?

A person who knows you, can answer questions about you, and is willing to recommend you for a job.

Whom can I ask to be a reference?

Here is a list of possibilities. Usually your references should be adults, and you should not use relatives.

Neighbors   Principal   Club Leaders
Teachers   Former Employers   Counselors
Your Minister   Doctor or Dentist   Your friends' parents
Friends of your parents

Whom could you use as references? Write them here.

_____   _____   _____   _____

What information should you get?

Name   Occupation
Address   How long they've known you
Phone

Here is a reference that Penny used to help her get a job:

REFERENCES (NOT FORMER EMPLOYERS OR RELATIVES)		
NAME	ADDRESS AND PHONE NO.	OCCUPATION
1) Mrs. Marie Jaubert	182 Fenton St Lakerton, Or 439-1240	Phone Co. Lineperson

Now it's your turn! Ask three people if they would be your references. Put the information in the blanks below. Then, you might want to put the information on your personal information card (next page).

REFERENCES (NOT FORMER EMPLOYERS OR RELATIVES)		
NAME	ADDRESS AND PHONE NO.	OCCUPATION
1)		
2)		
3)		

JOB-RELATED SKILLS

YOUR PERSONAL INFORMATION CARD

To fill out a job application form, you need to know some things about yourself. On this page is a personal information card. Fill it out carefully. Then check it for any mistakes. Make a copy of this card, and put it in your wallet. Take it with you when you to fill out a job application.

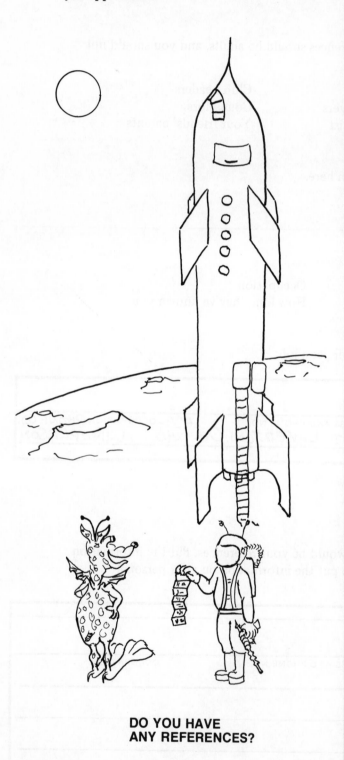

**DO YOU HAVE
ANY REFERENCES?**

PERSONAL INFORMATION

Name _____

Address _____

Phone _____ Birth ____/____/____

Social Security No. _____

WORK EXPERIENCE

Employer _____

Address _____

From: Mo/Yr _____ To: Mo/Yr _____

Job Description _____

_____ Salary _____

EDUCATION INFORMATION

(1) Elementary School _____

Address _____

Dates Attended _____ Grade Completed _____

(2) Junior High School _____

Address _____

Dates Attended _____ Grade Completed _____

(3) High School _____

Address _____

Dates Attended _____ Grade Completed _____

REFERENCES

(1) Name _____

Address _____

Phone _____

(2) Name _____

Address _____

Phone _____

(3) Name _____

Address _____

Phone _____

SELL YOURSELF! YOU'RE WORTH IT!

Sometimes you can get a job by putting a work-wanted card on a bulletin board in a school, store or other place of business. Or you can put an Employment Wanted ad in the Want Ads. Write your own work-wanted card. Look at the example below. Morrie used a work sheet to figure out all the information he wanted to put on his card. After reading Morrie's work sheet, fill in the work sheet for yourself. Then transfer the information in a neat, easy-to-read form to the work-wanted card below.

Student	What kind of work do you want?	List any jobs you've had.	Any other special things about you?	Put down your name, address and phone number.
Morrie	will do odd jobs; outdoor work. work with older people	2 years of mowing lawns; paper route; babysitting	age 17; enjoy school activities; have my own car	Morrie Amos 4435 S. Stork Skyway GA 43112 (912) 543-6925

WORK WANTED

Will do odd jobs. I enjoy outdoor work, or work with older people.

Worked 2 years mowing lawns, paper route, baby-sitting. 17 years old. Honest, dependable. Have my own car.

CONTACT: Morrie Amos
                4435 S. Stork
                Skyway, GA 43112
Telephone (after 3:30 p.m.) (912) 543-6925

MORRIE'S
CARD

WORK WANTED

YOUR
CARD

APPLICATION TERMS

Study these application form words and phrases, and their meanings. These words will come up over and over again in your job search.

1. **present address** — where you live now

2. **part-time** — working less than 40 hours per week

3. **full-time** — working 40 hours or more per week
   (some full-time work weeks are 35 hours)

4. **education** — the schools you went to

5. **references** — people who know you and can answer questions about you

6. **spouse** — a husband or wife

7. **dependents** — people you support (usually your children)

8. **physical disabilities** — injuries or weaknesses

9. **previous employment** — the work you have done before

10. **felony** — a serious crime

11. **state of health** — how your health is

12. **signature** — a person's name written by himself/herself

13. **skills** — things you learned or practiced to do well

14. **previous address** — where you lived before

15. **position** — the job you want to do

APPLICATION MATCH-UP

Match the term on the left with the meaning on the right.

1. present address   _____ people who can recommend you

2. part-time   _____ injuries or weaknesses

3. full-time   _____ a serious crime

4. education   _____ working less than 40 hours per week

5. references   _____ a person's name written by him/herself

6. spouse   _____ the schools you went to

7. dependents   _____ how your health is

8. physical disabilities   _____ things you learned or practiced to do well

9. previous employment   _____ working 40 hours or more per week

10. felony   _____ where you live now

11. state of health   _____ a husband or wife

12. signature   _____ the work you have done before

13. skills   _____ people you support (usually your children)

14. position   _____ where you lived before

15. previous address   _____ the job you want to do

Here are some rules to follow to help you fill out application forms:

1. PRACTICE
    Try filling out some different application forms before you go for a job.

2. BE PREPARED
    Some things you should bring with you are:
    a pencil and a pen
    your Social Security card
    a list of references
    your personal information card

3. READ THE APPLICATION CAREFULLY
    Mistakes will make the employer think that you can't follow directions.

4. ANSWER ALL QUESTIONS
    Don't leave blank spaces.

5. BE NEAT
    Don't cross things out. A messy application will make the employer think that you are sloppy.

6. CHECK THE APPLICATION
    When you are finished, look at the application to make sure you have filled it out correctly.

JOB-RELATED SKILLS

Look at these applications. If you could hire only one person:

Would you hire applicant no. 1? _____

Why or why not? _____

APPLICATION FOR EMPLOYMENT

(Discrimination because of age, race, creed, color or sex is prohibited by law.)

1

PERSONAL

LAST NAME	FIRST	MIDDLE
Martinez	Juan	

PRESENT ADDRESS	CITY & STATE	TELEPHONE NO.
55 Main St, Oakton	, NY	

DATE OF BIRTH	MARITAL STATUS	U.S. CITIZEN?	SOCIAL SECURITY NO.

WHO REFERRED YOU TO THIS COMPANY?
my brother

TYPE OF WORK DESIRED	APPROX. SALARY DESIRED
Stockperson	

EMPLOYMENT HISTORY (LIST MOST RECENT POSITION FIRST)

NAME OF EMPLOYER	ADDRESS	DATE STARTED
3 Brothers Restaurant	Amsterdam Ave, NY	1978

YOUR POSITION	STARTING SALARY
dishwasher	$3.40

DESCRIPTION OF DUTIES	DATE LEFT
	1980

REASON FOR LEAVING	SALARY AT LEAVING

EDUCATION

	NAME AND LOCATION OF SCHOOL	NO. OF YEARS ATTENDED	WHEN DID YOU LEAVE?	GRADUATED DEGREE
HIGH SCHOOL				
COLLEGE				
BUSINESS OR TRADE				

REFERENCES (NOT FORMER EMPLOYERS OR RELATIVES)

NAME	ADDRESS AND PHONE NO.	OCCUPATION
1)		
2)		

MILITARY

SERVED? ☐ IF YES,
☐ DATES: FROM_____ TO _____ DRAFT STATUS _____

PHYSICAL LIMITATIONS _____ EVER CONVICTED OF A FELONY? _____

IF YES, EXPLAIN _____

DATE OF APPLICATION	SIGNATURE

APPLICATION FOR EMPLOYMENT

(Discrimination because of age, race, creed, color or sex is prohibited by law.)

2

PERSONAL

LAST NAME	FIRST	MIDDLE
ESPADA	JOHN	

PRESENT ADDRESS	CITY & STATE	TELEPHONE NO.
16 N. STATE	OAKTON NY	457-2184

DATE OF BIRTH	MARITAL STATUS	U.S. CITIZEN?	SOCIAL SECURITY NO.
4/12/64	SINGLE		

WHO REFERRED YOU TO THIS COMPANY? MY TEACHER

TYPE OF WORK DESIRED	APPROX. SALARY DESIRED
STOCKPERSON	

EMPLOYMENT HISTORY (LIST MOST RECENT POSITION FIRST)

NAME OF EMPLOYER	ADDRESS	DATE
AL'S RESTAURANT		STARTED SUMMER '79
YOUR POSITION		STARTING SALARY
CASHIER		$4.05
DESCRIPTION OF DUTIES		DATE LEFT MAY '80
REASON FOR LEAVING		SALARY AT LEAVING

Would you hire applicant no. 2? _____

Why or Why not? _____

EDUCATION

	NAME AND LOCATION OF SCHOOL	NO. OF YEARS ATTENDED	WHEN DID YOU LEAVE?	GRADUATED DEGREE
HIGH SCHOOL	CENTRAL HIGH, OAKTON	3	WILL GRADUATE 1981	
COLLEGE				
BUSINESS OR TRADE				

REFERENCES (NOT FORMER EMPLOYERS OR RELATIVES)

NAME	ADDRESS AND PHONE NO.	OCCUPATION
1) MR. GEORGE HANSON	181 PELLETIER, OAKTON, NY	MINISTER
2)		

MILITARY

SERVED? ☐ IF YES,
☐ DATES: FROM_____ TO_____ DRAFT STATUS_____

PHYSICAL LIMITATIONS NONE EVER CONVICTED OF A FELONY? NO

IF YES, EXPLAIN _____

OCT 21, 1980	John Espada
DATE OF APPLICATION	SIGNATURE

APPLICATION FOR EMPLOYMENT
(Discrimination because of age, race, creed, color or sex is prohibited by law.)

3

PERSONAL

LAST NAME *Little*	FIRST *Paul*	MIDDLE
PRESENT ADDRESS *83 Wood...*	CITY & STATE *Mudow*	TELEPHONE NO *692-1361*
DATE OF BIRTH	MARITAL STATUS	U.S. CITIZEN?	SOCIAL SECURITY NO.

WHO REFERRED YOU TO THIS COMPANY? *Mr. Mudha*

TYPE OF WORK DESIRED *Stockperson*

APPROX. SALARY DESIRED *Scale*

EMPLOYMENT HISTORY (LIST MOST RECENT POSITION FIRST)

NAME OF EMPLOYER *Huston Munster*	ADDRESS	DATE STARTED *8/24/79*
YOUR POSITION		STARTING SALARY
DESCRIPTION OF DUTIES		DATE LEFT
REASON FOR LEAVING		SALARY AT LEAVING

EDUCATION

	NAME AND LOCATION OF SCHOOL	NO. OF YEARS ATTENDED	WHEN DID YOU LEAVE?	GRADUATED DEGREE
HIGH SCHOOL	*Huston General*	*2*	*Still there*	
COLLEGE				
BUSINESS OR TRADE				

Would you hire applicant no. 3? _____

Why or why not? _____

MILITARY

SERVED? ☐ IF YES,
☐ DATES: FROM _____ TO _____ DRAFT STATUS _____

PHYSICAL LIMITATIONS _____ EVER CONVICTED OF A FELONY? _____

IF YES, EXPLAIN _____

Paul Little

DATE OF APPLICATION	SIGNATURE

The application on the next page is filled in neatly and correctly. Study it and then try filling out the blank application on the next page.

APPLICATION FOR EMPLOYMENT

(Discrimination because of age, race, creed, color or sex is prohibited by law.)

PERSONAL

LAST NAME KORMAN FIRST ROCHELLE MIDDLE

PRESENT ADDRESS 301 N. LOCUST CITY & STATE INGLEWOOD CA 90301 TELEPHONE NO. 469-2381

DATE OF BIRTH 5/15/62 MARITAL STATUS SINGLE U.S. CITIZEN? YES SOCIAL SECURITY NO. 426-14-7982

WHO REFERRED YOU TO THIS COMPANY? MR. FRANCO, SCHOOL COUNSELOR

TYPE OF WORK DESIRED CLERK-TYPIST APPROX. SALARY DESIRED

EMPLOYMENT HISTORY (LIST MOST RECENT POSITION FIRST)

NAME OF EMPLOYER SOUND CITY ADDRESS 6423 BEVERLY BLVD L.A. DATE STARTED SEPT 1979

YOUR POSITION CASHIER STARTING SALARY $4.20/HR

DESCRIPTION OF DUTIES RING UP PURCHASES, DIRECT CUSTOMERS TO SALESPEOPLE DATE LEFT JUNE 1980

REASON FOR LEAVING STORE WENT OUT OF BUSINESS SALARY AT LEAVING $4.50/HR

EDUCATION

	NAME AND LOCATION OF SCHOOL	NO. OF YEARS ATTENDED	WHEN DID YOU LEAVE?	GRADUATED DEGREE
HIGH SCHOOL	LOS ANGELES HIGH SCHOOL, L.A.	2	SEPT. 1977 – PRESENT	
COLLEGE				
BUSINESS OR TRADE	TYPING I, SCHOOL WORK PROGRAM			

REFERENCES (NOT FORMER EMPLOYERS OR RELATIVES)

	NAME	ADDRESS AND PHONE NO.	OCCUPATION
1)	MR. VICTOR FRANCO	248 LYNNFIELD AVE ACTON 821-6340	SCHOOL COUNSELOR
2)	MRS. LUPE GOMEZ	12466 SANTA MONICA W. L.A 479-2357	DEPT. STORE MANAGER
3)			

MILITARY N/A
SERVED? ☐ IF YES,
☐ DATES: FROM_____TO_____DRAFT STATUS_____

PHYSICAL LIMITATIONS NONE EVER CONVICTED OF A FELONY? NO

IF YES, EXPLAIN_____

JULY 16, 1980
DATE OF APPLICATION

Rochelle Korman
SIGNATURE

101

JOB-RELATED SKILLS

APPLICATION FOR EMPLOYMENT

(Discrimination because of age, race, creed, color or sex is prohibited by law.)

PERSONAL

LAST NAME   FIRST   MIDDLE

PRESENT ADDRESS   CITY & STATE   TELEPHONE NO.

DATE OF BIRTH   MARITAL STATUS   U.S. CITIZEN?   SOCIAL SECURITY NO.

WHO REFERRED YOU TO THIS COMPANY?

TYPE OF WORK DESIRED   APPROX. SALARY DESIRED

EMPLOYMENT HISTORY (LIST MOST RECENT POSITION FIRST)

NAME OF EMPLOYER   ADDRESS   DATE STARTED

YOUR POSITION   STARTING SALARY

DESCRIPTION OF DUTIES   DATE LEFT

REASON FOR LEAVING   SALARY AT LEAVING

EDUCATION

	NAME AND LOCATION OF SCHOOL	NO. OF YEARS ATTENDED	WHEN DID YOU LEAVE?	GRADUATED DEGREE
HIGH SCHOOL				
COLLEGE				
BUSINESS OR TRADE				

REFERENCES (NOT FORMER EMPLOYERS OR RELATIVES)

NAME	ADDRESS AND PHONE NO.	OCCUPATION
1)		
2)		
3)		

MILITARY

    SERVED? ☐ IF YES,
            ☐ DATES: FROM_____TO _____DRAFT STATUS _____

PHYSICAL LIMITATIONS _____EVER CONVICTED OF A FELONY? _____

IF YES, EXPLAIN _____

_____   _____
    DATE OF APPLICATION   SIGNATURE

THE JOB INTERVIEW

Some basic rules for the job interview are listed here. Read each rule. Then look at the pictures below. The pictures show examples of keeping or breaking the rules. Write the rule below the picture that tells about it.

1. BE ON TIME for the interview.

2. GO ALONE. Don't bring friends or family members to the interview.

3. LOOK NEAT AND CLEAN.

4. SHAKE HANDS if the interviewer offers his/her hand.

5. LOOK AT THE INTERVIEWER during the interview. If you are looking around the room or at the floor, the interviewer will think you are not listening.

6. DON'T SMOKE OR CHEW GUM. You will make a better impression if you don't smoke, even if the interviewer offers you a cigarette

7. TALK SLOWLY AND CLEARLY.

8. BE READY TO SAY WHY YOU WANT THE JOB.

9. BE READY TO TELL ABOUT ANY WORK EXPERIENCE YOU HAVE.

10. THANK THE INTERVIEWER before you leave.

INTERVIEW DO'S AND DON'TS

Read these sentences. Each one describes something people have been known to do or say during job interviews. Cross out the sentences that tell what you *should not* do or say.

1. Bring your friends along to the interview.

2. "Thank you for interviewing me."

3. Smoke if you are offered a cigarette.

4. Come to the interview five minute late.

5. Remain standing until you are asked to sit down.

6. "I didn't like my last boss. He was always on my back."

7. Wear sloppy jeans and an old worn shirt to the interview.

8. "I guess I really don't have any experience for the job. I can't think of any."

9. Interrupt the interviewer.

10. "Hello, Mrs. Diaz. I'm Ron Healy. I have an appointment to be interviewed for the cashier's job."

11. "The first thing I want to know is, how much do you pay?"

12. Look at the interviewer as you talk.

13. Bring a pencil and pen in case you have to fill out any forms.

14. Ask questions about any important things the interviewer did not talk about.

15. When the the interviewer is talking, look around the room.

16. Leave your Personal Information Card at home.

The road to a job is paved with interview questions. Below are some questions the interviewer might ask. Write down how you would answer them.

INTERVIEWER SAYS:

1. "Yes, may I help you?"

You say: _____

2. "What kind of job are you interested in?"

You say: _____

3. "Why do you want to work?" (besides the money)

You say: _____

4. "What work have you done before?"

You say: _____

5. "Why do you think you would be good at this job?"

You say: _____

6. "If a customer complained to you, what would you do?"

You say: _____

7. "What days and hours can you work?"

You say: _____

8. "How much do you expect to earn?"

You say: _____

9. "Do you get along well with others?"

You say: _____

10. "Are you a good student? How are your grades? How is your attendance?"

You say: _____

11. "Why do you want to work here?"

You say: _____

TAXES, TAXES, TAXES

When you are hired, you will have to fill out a tax form like the one below. It is called a W-4 form. The W-4 form will tell your employer how much to take out of your paycheck for taxes. Your employer will withhold taxes at a certain basic rate unless you claim an "allowance" (See Question 4.) An allowance reduces the amount of taxes taken out of your paycheck. The usual allowance for a single person is 1. Your payroll office can give you more information.

Take a look at the sample W-4 below. Then fill out the empty form for yourself.

Form **W-4** (Rev. January 1986)	Department of the Treasury—Internal Revenue Service **Employee's Withholding Allowance Certificate**	OMB No. 1545-0010 Expires: 11-30-87

1 Type or print your full name
MARY JO SAVOL

2 Your social security number
448-27-8952

Home address (number and street or rural route)
316 MIDLAND AVE.

City or town, state, and ZIP code
ANN, ILLINOIS   64289

3 Marital Status
☒ Single   ☐ Married
☐ Married, but withhold at higher Single rate
Note: If married, but legally separated, or spouse is a nonresident alien, check the Single box.

4 Total number of allowances you are claiming (from line F of the worksheet on page 2) *1*

5 Additional amount, if any, you want deducted from each pay . . . . $

6 I claim exemption from withholding because (see instructions and check boxes below that apply):
  a ☒ Last year I did not owe any Federal income tax and had a right to a full refund of **ALL** income tax withheld, **AND**
  b ☒ This year I do not expect to owe any Federal income tax and expect to have a right to a full refund of **ALL** income tax withheld. If both a and b apply, enter the year effective and "EXEMPT" here ► Year 19*89* *EXEMPT*
  c If you entered "EXEMPT" on line 6b, are you a full-time student? . . . . ☒Yes ☐No

Under penalties of perjury, I certify that I am entitled to the number of withholding allowances claimed on this certificate, or if claiming exemption from withholding, that I am entitled to claim the exempt status.
Employee's signature ► *Mary Jo Savol*   Date ► *June 19*   19 *89*

Form **W-4** (Rev. January 1986)	Department of the Treasury—Internal Revenue Service **Employee's Withholding Allowance Certificate**	OMB No. 1545-0010 Expires: 11-30-87

1 Type or print your full name

2 Your social security number

Home address (number and street or rural route)

City or town, state, and ZIP code

3 Marital Status
☐ Single   ☐ Married
☐ Married, but withhold at higher Single rate
Note: If married, but legally separated, or spouse is a nonresident alien, check the Single box.

4 Total number of allowances you are claiming (from line F of the worksheet on page 2) . . . .

5 Additional amount, if any, you want deducted from each pay . . . . $

6 I claim exemption from withholding because (see instructions and check boxes below that apply):
  a ☐ Last year I did not owe any Federal income tax and had a right to a full refund of **ALL** income tax withheld, **AND**
  b ☐ This year I do not expect to owe any Federal income tax and expect to have a right to a full refund of **ALL** income tax withheld. If both a and b apply, enter the year effective and "EXEMPT" here ► Year 19
  c If you entered "EXEMPT" on line 6b, are you a full-time student? . . . . ☐Yes ☐No

Under penalties of perjury, I certify that I am entitled to the number of withholding allowances claimed on this certificate, or if claiming exemption from withholding, that I am entitled to claim the exempt status.
Employee's signature ►   Date ►   19

WHAT A MESS!

Name: Sloppy Sergio

Occupation: Cook and counter person at Paradise
Sandwich Shop.

Description

Hat:	stained with grease
Hair:	not combed
Face:	needs a shave
Shirt:	stained with coffee
Apron:	has a hole in it
Hands:	dirty
Pants:	grimy
Shoes:	coming apart

Would you buy a hamburger from this
man? _____

If not, why not? _____

_____

Would you go back to a place that would let
such a worker wait on customers? _____

If not, why not? _____

_____

Check (√) the items of your personal appearance
that an employer would want you to be careful
about.

_____ dirty fingernails	_____ dirty shirt
_____ dirty hands	_____ dirty neck
_____ unshaven face	_____ dirty ears
_____ unshined shoes	_____ baggy pants
_____ hair not combed	_____ bad breath
_____ sloppy clothes	_____ missing buttons
_____ dirty cuffs	_____ hair too long
_____ dirty collar	_____ dandruff
_____ dirty hair	_____ other: _____

RULES, RULES, RULES

Every company has Health and Safety rules which the employee must follow. Health rules are made to keep people from getting sick and to keep things clean and sanitary. Safety rules are made to prevent accidents and injuries to you and to other people.

Below is a list of Health and Safety rules used in different kinds of jobs. Put an H in front of Health rules. Put an S in front of Safety rules.

_____ When spray painting, wear a face mask.

_____ Throw away used bandages.

_____ Do not smoke near a gas pump.

_____ Wear a hairnet when working around food.

_____ Do not spray insecticide in a closed room.

_____ Use a wheelchair when moving patients.

_____ Wear non-skid shoes in the kitchen area.

_____ Wash hands after using the ditto machine.

_____ Do not wear jewelry on the job.

_____ Watch carefully when operating moving machinery.

_____ Read directions before operating machinery.

List the Health and Safety rules that your employer wants you to follow on the job:

1. _____

2. _____

3. _____

4. _____

5. _____

Have you ever been in an accident at work? If you have, fill out the form below. If you have never been hurt at work, write about an accident that you have seen.

Job:

What Accident Happened?:

How Could It Have Been Prevented?:

WHAT DOES MY PAYCHECK SAY?

Getting your paycheck is one of the nicest parts of your job. Understanding your paycheck can be a little bit harder. The words and meanings below will help you figure it out.

Pay period ending: the last working day for which you were paid.

Hours: the number of hours you worked in the pay period.

Gross earnings: the total amount of money you have earned in this pay period.

Net earnings: the amount of money you will take home for this pay period.

Gross earnings: amount of money you have earned in the pay period	*Net earnings:* amount of money you take home in this pay period
$5.00 wage per hour x 12 hours you have worked $60.00 gross earnings	$60.00 gross earnings −$10.00 deductions $50.00 net earnings

Deductions: the amount of money taken from your paycheck (federal, state and local taxes, FICA, uniforms, health insurance, and other things).

Federal: the tax you pay to the United States government.

State: the tax you pay to your state government.

Local: the tax you pay to your local government.

F.I.C.A.: the tax you pay to the Social Security system.

Year-to-Date Earnings: the total (gross) amount of money you have earned this year on this job.

Year-to-Date Taxes: the total amount of taxes you have paid this year on this job to the following: federal, state, local governments, and F.I.C.A.

JOB-RELATED SKILLS

Now read Jim's paycheck stub and answer the questions below.

323-64-8067	**BEEF VILLAGE**	

JAMES PLACERES   <u>STATEMENT OF EARNINGS AND DEDUCTIONS.</u>

PAY PERIOD ENDING	11/10/86		HOURS WORKED	20

GROSS EARNINGS	TAXES				TOTAL DEDUCTIONS	NET PAY
	FEDERAL	F.I.C.A.	STATE	LOCAL		
90.80	10.35	5.57	2.27	.00	18.19	$72.61
666.87	63.63	40.88	16.67	.00		$72 | 61
YEAR TO DATE						AMOUNT OF CHECK

DETACH AND KEEP FOR YOUR RECORDS

1. What is Jim's Social Security number? _____

2. When did Jim's pay period end? _____

3. What were Jim's gross earnings? _____

4. What were Jim's deductions? _____

5. How much did Jim pay to Social Security this pay period? _____

6. What was Jim's Year-to-Date state tax? _____

7. What was Jim's federal tax? _____

8. What was Jim's Year-to-Date Social Security tax? _____

9. What was Jim's state tax this pay period? _____

10. What was Jim's Year-to-Date federal tax? _____

11. What were Jim's net earnings? _____

12. How many hours did Jim work this pay period? _____